THE INQUISIT GARDENER

by

Robin Rowlinson
&
Jonathan MacDonald

QUIZ BOOK
VOLUME ONE

R&M PUBLISHING 2004

© Robin Rowlinson and Jonathan
MacDonald

First Published 2004
R&M PUBLISHING

ISBN 0-9548292-0-4

Printed in the UK by
J. W. Arrowsmith Ltd, Bristol

THIS BOOK IS DEDICATED TO
EMILIE, ANNA, LUCY

&

GILLESPIE AND ALICE

INTRODUCTION

For many years gardeners have had an inquisitive mind. Often a gardener's knowledge of the subject is as important as the ability to garden itself. We hear often of heated debates at garden clubs on what plants are called, when to sow, how to grow and so on. These differences are what make's gardening fun. With this in mind we have created a book that aims not to be an authority on the subject but to offer a light hearted and enjoyable way of developing knowledge and continuing the debate. Perhaps if you are the ultimate gardening snob this might help you a little in your arguments. No real gardener would ever claim to know it all. We hope you enjoy it and look out in the shops for Volume 2.

Jonathan and Rob

July 2004

CONTENTS

1. THESE TREES ARE A BREEZE

1. What is the oldest living tree on earth?

2. Which wood was traditionally used for making barrel hoops?

3. Cogs on millwheels were made from which tree?

4. Abele is another name for what tree?

5. Why is a horse chestnut so called?

6. Cottoner, mealy tree and whipcrop are local names for what tree?

7. What is the largest tree in the world?

8. What is the tallest tree in the world?

9. What tree is regarded as being the worlds largest living organism?

10. What tree is regarded as being resistant to all known pests and diseases?

2. IN THE SHRUBBERY

1. What shrubs do Gypsies traditionally make clothes pegs from?

2. Blackthorn is used to make what Irish fighting stick?

3. Who is regarded as being the Father of English garden roses introducing the first cultivars in 1969?

4. What shrub will be in flower 12 months a year hence the saying "you should only make love when the _____ is in flower"?

5. What is the odd one out - Pieris, Enkianthus, Azalea, Syringa, Camellia, Crinodendron?

6. Which shrub is worn or carried in commemoration of William Shakespeare's birth?

7. The stems of Chinese Wisteria (W. sinensis) twine in which direction, clockwise or anticlockwise?

8. The Chastelamb tree is the classical name for which shrub?

9. What is the meaning of the term Cultivar?

10. Who is the odd girl out: Rosemary, Daphne, Ivy, Heather, Nigella, Erica?

"Wearing all that weight
Of learning lightly like a flower"
Tennyson

3. PERENNIAL CHALLENGE

1. What was the ancient name for Hellebore?

2. The dried stems of which perennial were used to make childrens pea shooters?

3. The leaves of Angelica, Coltsfoot, Hogweed, Meadowsweet and Rosebay willowherb have what in common?

4. Odd one out: Chrysanthemums, Daisies, Helenium, Osteospermum, Helianthus, Yarrow?

5. What's the largest herbaceous perennial in the world?

6. What perennial is regarded as being the favourite food source of the bumble bee?

7. Odd one out: bulleyana, elwesii, confusa, graminea, iberica, japonica, delavayi?

8. The blazing star (Liatris spp.) is renowned for this unusual flowering characteristic?

9. If your Hosta's are albescent what will happen to them?

10. If you cross a Heuchera and a Tiarella what do you get?

"Have you seen but a bright Lily grow
Before rude hands have touch'd it
Have you mark'd but the fall O' the snow
Before the soil hath smutch'd it?"
Jonson

4. ANNUAL HORRIBILIS

1. Who invented park bedding schemes?

2. Shakespeare referred to them in Midsummer's Night Dream as 'love in idleness'. What popular bedding plant was the bard referring to?

3. Where would you typically place a Lysimachia nummularia?

4. If you had poached eggs in your garden what would you be growing?

5. What is dusty miller?

6. Odd one out: Ageratum houstonianum, Lobularia maritime, Lycopersicum esculentum, Gazania rigens, Antirrhinum majus, Torenia fournieri?

7. AMG is the curse of the green keeper, what annual does it refer to?

8. What would you do with a Capsicum annuum?

9. Odd one out: Alcea rosea, Bellis perrenis, Digitalis purpurea, Erysium cherei, Zinnia elagans, Senicio vulgaris?

10. Is parsley an annual, biennial or perennial?

"Fair daffodils, we weep to see
You haste away so soon
As yet the early-rising sun
Has not attain'd his noon"

Herrick

5. GENERAL CROSSWORD #1

ACROSS

1/ Tree _ _ glauca (6,9)
8/ Pollen producer (6)
10/ Tall grass (3)
11/ Panama disease affects which plant (6)
13/ Common nettle (6)
14/ Bulbous house plant (9)
15/ Chestnut (8)
16/ Sods (4)
18/ Friendly aerator (4)
19/ Plant of the genus Boraginaceae (6)
21/ Rosaceous perennial (4)
22/ Poor man orchid (12)
25/ Iridaceous perennial (12)
27/ Halimium x cistus (13)
30/ Sneezeweed (8)
31/ Water soldier (10)

DOWN

2/ Summer fruit (9)
3/ Top part of a graft (5)
4/ Jungle climber (5)
5/ Liliaceous plant (12)
6/ Australasian shrub *Myrtaceae* (12)
7/ Common spring roadside weed (10)
9/ Arbor vitea (5)
12/ Plant of the onion family (6)
17/ Herbaceous perennial *Ranunculaceae* (6)
20/ Plantain lily (5)

23/ Catchfly (7)
24/ Loosetrife (7)
26/ Salad herb (6)
28/ Common herb (4)
29/ Common yellow flowering shrub (4)

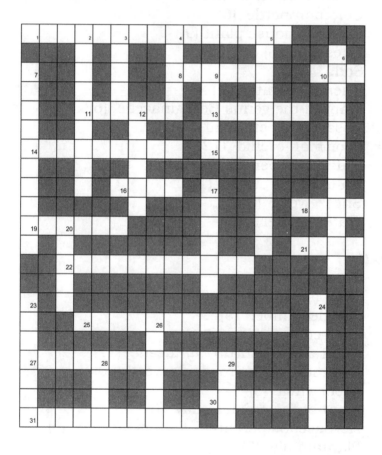

6. THE HERB GARDEN

1. Saffron comes from the dried stamens of which flowering bulb?

2. Cilantro shares its name with what common herb?

3. Which herb is the main ingredient of Pesto sauce?

4. What's the recommended method of growing mint in the garden?

5. Tanacetum vulgare (garden tansy) is traditionally known as which herb?

6. Petroselinum crispum is better known as?

7. If you distill and bottle English wheat, Juniper berries, Coriander, Orange peel, Lemon peel, Angelica root, Orris root, Cardamom and water, what will you produce?

8. A small muslin parcel of herbs for infusion with soups and stews is more commonly know as?

9. What family does Mustard belong to?

10. Before its modern name what was know as "Redcole"?

7. VEGETABLE SOUP

1. What vegetable should you never eat green?

2. What plant pigment is abundant in Carrots?

3. Pisum is the Latin name for what vegetable?

4. If you eat broccoli, what part of the plant would you be eating?

5. The word onion is derived from the Latin "Unio". What does it mean?

6. Odd one out please: King Edward, Wilja, Pentland Squire, Marris Piper, James Grieve, Norking Russet, Ilona?

7. St Valery and Early Nantes are which type of vegetable?

8. To what family do onions belong?

9. Brassica bullata, Brassica capitata, Brassica botrytis, Brassica major, Brassica caulo-rapa, Brassica rapa. Which of the above is a Brussel sprout?

10. Which vegetable shares its family with tobacco, tomato, deadly nightshade, Tabasco sauce, aubergine and Petunia?

8. FUNGI FINDER

1. What is the largest fungus know to man?

2. What is the Amanita phalloides claim to fame?

3. Odd one out: Lepista saeva, Agaricus augustus, Boletus badeus, Inocybe patouillardii, Calocybe gambosa, Caprinus comatus?

4. What would you do with an Agaricus campestris?

5. Tuber magnatum is best known as what?

6. King Alfred's cakes/cramp balls (Daldinia concentrica) when dried are used for making this?

7. Molds, yeasts, mushrooms, and toadstools are lacking in a substance that plants are not. What is it?

8. Callorina fusarioides grows on the stems of which dead weed?

9. What do you call a mushroom at a party?

10. What are Marasmius oreades better know as?

9. DO YOU KNOW YOUR PLANTSMANSHIP

Match the plant to the plant hunter.
Clues are jumbled up.

PLANT HUNTER	ANSWERS	CLUES
Sir Joseph Hooker		Cryptomeria japonica
Nathanial Wallich		Himalayan Birch
Englebert Kampher		Himalayan White Pine
William Kerr		Chinese larch
Robert Fortune		Clematis montana
Grigori Nicolevich Potanin		Gingko biloba
John Gould Veitch		Magnolia stellata
George André Soulié		Chinese Juniper
Victor Jacquemont		Buddleja
Lady Amherst		Doedar Cedar

10. UNWANTED GUESTS

1. What causes "Oak Apples"?

2. Calcium deficiency due to dry conditions in the orchard is likely to cause which disorder?

3. Onion white rot is known to the vegetable grower as what disease?

4. If you see "Frass" on your plants what damage are you likely to see along with it?

5. What is regarded as the UK's most problematic garden pest today?

6. Greenback on tomatoes is caused by what?

7. Arion hortensis is more commonly known as which garden pest?

8. The fungus Ceratocystis ulmi was the cause of widespread damage during the 1970/1980's in the UK. What did it destroy?

9. Phytophthora infestans or potato blight was cause of the Irish potato famine? What was the main reason for its rapid spread?

10. Many gardeners have had their day ruined by Vespula vulgaris. What is it's real name?

11. GENERAL CROSSWORD #2

ACROSS

1/   ____ fly trap, carnivorous (5)
2/   Productive time in the garden (6)
4/   Chinese border perennial (6)
6/   Seeds of Citrus fruit (4)
8/   Vegatables (7)
9/   Shrub of the genus Syringa (5)
10/   Herb of the mint family (6)
11/   Depth of a spade (4)
13/   Eleagnus's (9)
17/   Colourful house plant (6)
18/   Brassica (7)
20/   Clivia, hymenocallis etc. (5)
22/   Abu Hassan, Arabian mystery etc. (6)
23/   Sows seed by hand (10)
24/   Salad fruit (7)
25/   Evergreen or deciduous perennials (8)
28/   Garden tools (4)
29/   False (6)
32/   Hopefully your cutting will have done this (6)
34/   Woody plants (6)
37/   Tree of the genus Tillia (4)
38/   e.g. Carex (5)
41/   Garden reptile (5)
42/   Outer case of a filbert (5)
44/   e.g. Sycamore (4)
45/   Grapevine (5)
46/   Scottish Raspberry (8)

DOWN

1/ Arkwright beauty or yellow bedder (5)
3/ Growing medium (4,4)
4/ First vegetable to be canned (3)
5/ Garden pests (6)
7/ Land measure (4)
8/ Aments (7)
12/ Rorippa nasturtium aquaticum (10)
14/ Delphineums (9)
15/ Garden insect (6,3)
16/ Swarming tropical insect pests (6)
17/ Kentish, Butler and Gunslebert are what (7)
19/ Seed of wheat or barley (5)
21/ Clumps of trees (6)
26/ Helianthemum (8)
27/ Adult caterpillar (4)
28/ Formal row of shrubs (5)
30/ Succory (8)
31/ Strongly scented cutflower (7)
33/ Showy annuals (6)
35/ Snails belong to this genus (5)
36/ Telham _____ (Campanula) (6)
39/ Fraxinus excelsior (3)
40/ Pulse (4)
43/ _____ in a mist (Nigella) (4)

"There is a garden that I dream of.
The garden of your hear"
Teschemacher

GENERAL CROSSWORD #2

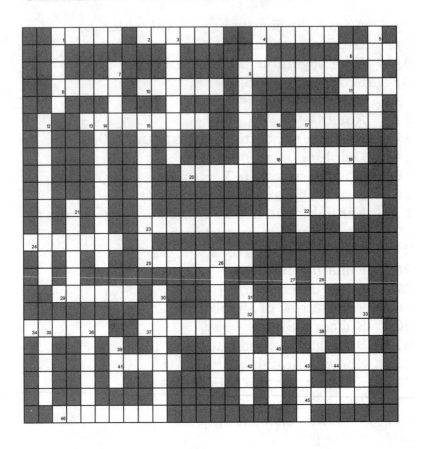

"A child said *what is the grass?* fetching
it to one with full hands"

Whitman

12. WEED THESE OUT

1. The giant hogweed (Heracleum mantegazzianum), UK's largest weed, belongs to which family?

2. The leaf of the Rumex obtusifolius is used to soothe the pain caused by Urtica dioica. What are they?

3. What weeds can really stick to you?

4. Odd one out: Fizz-gig, Sleepy dose, Stinking alisander, Stinking davies, Yellow weed, St. James-wort, Stinking nanny, Horehound, Staggerwort, Dog standard, Cankerwort, Stammerwort?

5. Creeping, Milk, Sow, Golden, Plymouth, and Spear are all what?

6. What weed is the enemy of the Green-keeper?

7. Where does the word Dandelion come from?

8. What is regarded as the "worlds worst weed"?

9. To date what the most leaves found on a clover?

10. What is the definition of a weed?

13. PRICKLY CUSTOMERS

1. What famous alcoholic drink is produced from the Agave succulent?

2. Odd one out please: Alluadia, Gymnocalycium, Aztekium, Echinocereus, Parodia, Quiabentia Carnegia?

3. The century plant, Agave americana can live for how long?

4. Lithops or Livingstones, belong to which family?

5. Carnegiea gigantean is more commonly known as which cactus?

6. Schlumbergera and Zygocactus go by which common name?

7. Who would you not wish to sit on a Echinocactus grusonii?

8. What cactus became well known in the 1970's books by Carlos Castenada?

9. You will see Echivera setosa in UK park annual bedding schemes. What's their common name?

10. Which well known succulent is used in soaps, shampoos and cosmetics?

14. FAMOUS FACES IN THE GARDEN

Rearrange the jumbled dates to match these famous gardeners.

FAMOUS GARDENER	ANSWER	JUMBLED DATES
Gertrude Jekyll		(1752-1818)
Humphrey Repton		(23-79AD)
Rosemary Very		(1608-1662)
Sir Joseph Paxton		(1843 - 1932)
Pliny the elder		(1803-1865)
Carl Linnaeus		(1843 - 1932)
Vita Sackville-West		(1752-1818)
Brown, Lancelot ('Capability')		(1919-2001)
Tradescant, John		(1913-1988),
Gertrude Jekyll		(1707-1778)

15. THE ABUNDANT ORCHID

1. The Aztec Indians cultivated the Orchid tlilxochitl, today it is widely known as?

2. The smallest flower on an orchid is 500 microns in diameter. How small is that?

3. Many orchids are pollinated by what is called "copulatory" flowers. What does this mean?

4. Odd one out: Sympodials, monopodials, terrestrials, epiphytes, trilobites, lithophytes?

5. All orchids have something in common numerically. What is it?

6. *Grammmatophyllum speciosum* or tiger orchid is renowned for which characteristic?

7. How many orchids occur in the wild in the UK?

8. Every orchid has a Labellum, what does this mean?

9. If an orchid is said to be terrestrial where does it live?

10. What is regarded as best and easiest orchid to grow in the home?

16. LAWN TO BE PROUD OF

1. For what purpose would you use a hollow tine?

2. If you discover a Melolontha melolontha in your lawn, what have you found?

3. The prototype of the first hover mower is based on what common household object?

4. Who invented the first lawnmower in 1830?

5. Other than grass, what other plant can be used to create a lawn?

6. Botanically why is it possible to have a lawn?

7. What is the nutritional analysis of lawn clippings?

8. What metal do you use to remove moss from your lawn?

9. What are the small piles of soil found on your lawn called?

10. Where does the word lawn originate from?

17. BULBWORD #3

ACROSS

1/   Group of daffodils (8)
2/   Spring saffron (11)
7/   Quamash (8)
10/   Allium siculum (14)
13/   Dracunculus (6,4)
14/   See 2 down
15/   31 down and 33 across,
        Ornithogalum umbellatum (4,2,9)
16/   See 9 down
19/   Crocosmia (10)
20/   Plant of the Iris family (7)
21/   Canna lily (6,4)
22/   See 11 down
23/   _____ plant (Arisarum) (5)
24/   Bulb related to Hippeastrum (10)
26/   See 12 down
27/   Baboon root (7)
30/   Butterfly iris (6,10)
32/   5 down, Anemone coronaria (7,7)
33/   See 15 across
34/   and 17 down, Asphodelus lutea (6,3)

DOWN

1/ Arisaema triphyllum (4,2,3,6)

2/ 14 across, 18 down
Phaliophlops bermudianum
(4,4,5)

3/ See 8 down

4/ Arum lilies USA (6)

5/ See 32 across

6/ The Tenby daffodil (9,10)

8/ 3 down Vallota (11,4)

9/ And 16 across, Eranthis
hymalis (6,7)

11/ And 22 across, Hyacinthus
orientalis albulus (5,8)

12/ Easy to grow indoor lily (3,7,6)

17/ See 34 across

18/ See 2 down

25/ Merrybells (8)

28/ _____ brush, Haemanthus
albiflos (5)

29/ _____ flower, Dierama (4)

32/ See 15 across

"Wel loved he garleek, oynons, and eek
lekes
And for to drinken strong wyn, reed as
blood"

Chaucer

BULBWORD #3

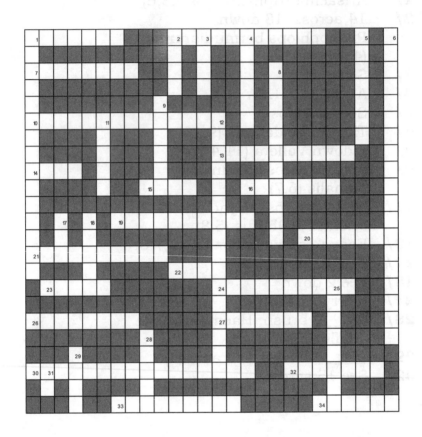

18. COMPOST BREAKDOWN

1. Odd one out: Grass, eggshells, leaves, roots, potato peelings, orange peelings, shredded newspaper, sawdust.

2. What is JIP ?

3. Coir is made from which tropical plant?

4. What type of compost would you grow heathers in?

5. Imidacloprid when used as an additive in compost controls what garden pest?

6. Sphagnum moss peat can hold 5, 10,15,20 or 25 times its own weight in water?

7. What can you add to compost to lower the pH ?

8. What can you add to compost to raise the pH ?

9. Where should you site a compost bin?

10. Where do the roots of plants grow?

19. PEACH, PLUM OR PEAR

Match up the peach, plum or pears to
the correct variety?

VARIETY OF PEACH, PLUM OR PEAR	ANSWER
Kieffer	
Rio Oso Gem	
Chickasaw	
Weaver	
Belle of Georgia	
Dixie Red	
Winter Nelis	
Halehaven	
Victoria	
Desoto	
Buerre Hardy	
Reine Claude	
Triogem	
Elberta	
Coyenne du Comice	
Williams	
Lombard	
Bartlet	
Sunhigh	
Anjou	

20. MEGAQUIZ #1

1. How do we more commonly know the seed of Anacardium occidentale?

2. Artimisia dracunculus is better known as which herb?

3. What is tarrow (Colocasia esculenta) used for by the pacific islanders?

4. Which plant does the drug Socotrine come from?

5. The bark of the Oak amongst other trees is rich in a chemical used in treating leather, what is it?

6. What is a stipule?

7. In botany what does stipate mean?

8. A plant that is polycotyledonous has how many seed leaves?

9. The tart tasting fruit of Ribes grossularia is more commonly known as what?

10. Gale is another name for which plant?

11. How is a flower having three carpels described botanically?

12. What does fastigate mean?

13. The pericarp is which part of a seed?

14. When telling the time using a dandelion clock, what is the botanically correct name for the fluffy seeds that disperse on the breeze?

15. What is cuckoo spit?

16. What is and where would you find, Llano?

17. Tanacetum vulgare goes by which common name?

18. The Tanghin tree comes from which part of the world?

19. In Botany what does uncinate mean?

20. The drug Laudanum is prepared from which plant?

21. What is the main ingredient in the dish Frumenty?

22. What does Frugiferous mean?

23. Zingiber officinale is more commonly known as?

24. The collective fallen fruits of forest trees such as the oak and beech are known as?

25. The screw pines belong to which genus?

26. Rue belongs to which genus?

27. What is a seckel?

28. What does glandiferous mean?

29. What is the common name of Crategus monogyna?

30. What is a melampod?

31. What type of vegetable is a Frijole?

32. Where would you find a Knur?

33. How do we commonly know the turnip stemmed cabbage Brassica oleracea caulorapa?

34. Laurastinus is another name for which plant?

35. What does Malvaceous mean?

36. What is Nebbuk?

37. To which genus does the evening primrose belong?

38. Curly like a vine tendril?

39. What is the common name of Pyrus cydonia

40. In nomenclature what does Dendron mean?

41. How is Sorbus aria more commonly known?

42. Terebinth or Pistacia terebinthus. Common name please?

43. Which plant was believed to scream when pulled from the ground?

44. Which rope making fibre is prepared from Musa textiles?

45. What is bladderwrack?

46. What is a spinney?

47. Squill is the common name for which plant?

48. What kind of turf is Liriope muscari more commonly known as?

49. Acalycine plants don't have these?

50. What happens when plasmolosis takes place?

51. Punicaceae has only one member, what is it?

52. What is the common name of Raphanus sativus?

53. Odd one out: Black, Italian, Carniolan, Ruby tailed, Vestel cuckoo, moss carda, large redtailed?

54. Where would you find an apical bud?

55. If a plant becomes etoliated what will you see?

56. The survival of plant parts during the dormant season is described as what?

57. Sowing seeds individually in pre-determined spacing is known as?

58. In tomato plants what name do we give to the fast growing lateral shoot preceeding a truss?

59. What is a Langley gage?

60. What is a lady Sudeley?

21. FLOWERING PLANTS CROSSWORD #4

ACROSS

1/   See 6
2/   Ranunculus (9,7)
6/   and 1, Trollius (5,6)
7/   See 11
9/   _____ primrose (Oenothera) (7)
10/   Achillea (7)
11/   and 7, Campanula
       cochlearifolia (5,8)
13/   15 down and 32 across,
       ___ /___/___ vine (cobaea) (3,3,6)
14/   see 4 down
17/   Everlasting flower (11)
18/   See 26 down
19/   See 26 down
21/   See 26 down
23/   See 9
25/   Verbascum (7)
28/   Corn lily (4)
29/   Aruncus (5,5)
30/   33,36,25 down, Nigella,
       (4,2,1,4)
31/   See 13
32/   and 27 down, Tiarella (4,6)
34/   Pulmonaria (8)
35/   Linnaea (4,6)

DOWN

1/   Matricaria (8)
2/   see 3
3/   and 2, Saponaria (8,3)
4/   and 14 across, unusual
          Dahlia (common name
          Giraffe) (6,8,6)
5/   Sedum (9)
8/   See 12 down
10/   Aster (10,5)
12/   and 8, Pleione (7,6)
15/   see 13 across
16/   Tritonia (7,4)
17/   Love lies bleeding (10)
18/   see 26
20/   Scilla (6)
22/   Prunella (4,4)
24/   Tradescantia virginiana (10)
25/   See 30
26/   18,19 across and 21 across,
          Dicentra (4,2,3,4)
27/   See 32 across
33/   See 30 across

"The dew that on the violet lies
Mocks the dark lustre of thine eyes"

Scott

FLOWERING PLANTS CROSSWORD #4

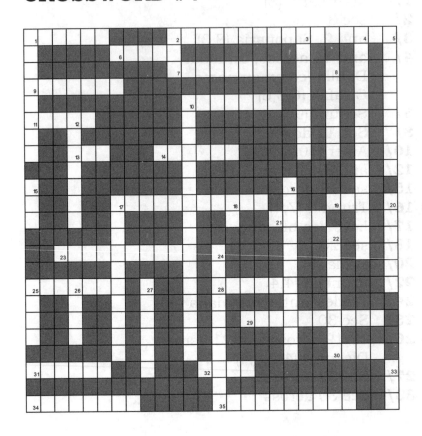

22. INCREASING YOUR STOCK

1. What part of a grafted plant is the scion?

2. How do you propagate tomato plants?

3. What plant hormone regulates root initiation?

4. How do you propagate roses commercially?

5. What is used to propagate ferns?

6. Odd one out: Hard, soft, tip, seed, root, leaf, offset, division, layering?

7. What is the botanical name given to a plant with 2 seed leaves?

8. Why wound the base of hard wood cuttings?

9. When would you use an interstock?

10. What plant do you scoop?

23. FIND 40 FUNGI (CROSSWORD GRID)

Answers run up, down, left and right and diagonally. See if you can find them.

Horse mushroom
Deceiver
Saffron milkcap
Slippery jack
Morel
False deathcap
Red cracked boletus
Giant puffball
Tree ear
Hen of the wood
Sulphur tuft
Amethyst deceiver
Jews ear
Blewit
Blusher
Pennybun
Horn of plenty
Matsutake
Panther
Saint Georges mushroom

Brick cap
Velvet shank
Beefsteak fungus
Hedgehog fungus
Honeyfungus
Wax cap
Black morel
Stickybun
Trompette desmorts
Shaggy ink cap
Fairy rings
Boletus
Truffle
The sickener
Bootlaces
Cep
Parasol
Fly agaric
Oyster
Ergot

FIND 40 FUNGI

```
h o r s e m u s h r o o m f m p a c k c i r b
e w b l u s h e r d e r o d g e l e u l b t p
d e c e i v e r h z w e r f j p e d d h v r k
g w s g n i r y r i a f e q n u y k p o v o m
e t h e p r i n c e v e l v e t s h a n k m o
h g w s a f f r o n m i l k c a p r c e m p o
o h g u b o l e t u s t p r t w b m h y r e r
g w h t l g r t i w e l b r m r i y t f e t h
f s t e a k f u n g u s u l o p m g a u v t s
u g h l c e p r m t p f v w s n i r e n i e u
n g e o k w p h o a f n n s o a d e d g e d m
g i s b m f u g r l w r t t n p y h e u c e s
u w i d o h r a e k o t u t a t e t s s e s e
s s c e r e s p n l p o p c n n b n l f d m g
h r k k e o d u l h m o k e o f l a a d t o r
p e e c l f b r p e l n l f l r u p f w s r o
a y n a p y i r d y i p t y e g s w f p y t e
c w e r k m a d p y f h a t w k h y h d h s g
x a r c p e e o g o e g s g e l e u l b t f t
a l i d e i r g n w a y f p u k r f k p e g n
w t r e p e a r o r o t e k a t u s t a m p i
s g r r z h o o i b o o t l a c e s o g a l a
z t e g s h d c t g h k c a j y r e p p i l s
```

24. COLLOQUIALISMS

The county name and common name are correct.
Can you un-jumble the counties to which they
belong.

COUNTY NAME	ANSWER	COUNTY	COMMON NAME
Shiners		Cheshire	Lord and ladies
Skeet plant		Shetland	Hogweed
Shoes and stockings		East Anglia	Birds foot trefoil
Vervine		Shetland	Motherwort
Witchen		Nottingham-shire	Rowan
Minerac		Peak district	Selfheal
Lady's milk sile		Manx	Lungwort
Honey – sookies		County Offaly	Lousewort
Everlasting sin		Gwent	Slender speedwell

COUNTY NAME	ANSWER	COUNTY	COMMON NAME
Fairies petticoat		Kent	Foxglove
Dead mans bells		Cornwall	Sea campion
Black knobs		Sussex	Alder fruits
Ascension		Gloucestershire	Groundsel
Money in both pockets		Shropshire	Honesty
Mogue Tobin		Morayshire	Corn marigold
Old mans pepper		Cheshire	Meadow Sweet
St John of Beverly		East Anglia	Primroses
Tom – bacca		Humberside	Travellers joy
Wavverin leaf		County Carlow	Greater plantain
God's hand leaf		Worcestershire	Valarian

25. CHRISTMAS CRACKER

1. Euphorbia pulcherrima is the botanical name for what well know Christmas pot plant?

2. What do you get under Viscum album?

3. What traditional table decoration is made from Betula pendula?

4. What common name do we know the popular perennial Helleborus niger as?

5. What famous song do we hear when we sing "The Ilex aquifolium and the Hedera helix" ?

6. Picea abies is regarded as being what traditional plant?

7. Vaccinium macrocarpon is the accompaniment for what Christmas fayre?

8. Salvia officianlis and Allium cepa are found together where?

9. In what do we find Prunus domestica?

10. Who's for some Pastinaca sativa?

26. HOUSEPLANTS CROSSWORD #5

ACROSS

1/   Foliage house plant ____ dyeranus (13)
7/   See 23
10/   Gesnaria cardinalis (genus) (13)
11/   _____ diversifolia, the indoor oak (9)
14/   and 22, Guzmania lingulata minor (common name) (7,4)
16/   Man made hybrid orchid (12)
20/   and 33, Jacobinia carnea (common name) (5,5)
21/   Howea belmorrana, _____ palm (5)
23/   and 7, Ornamental pepper (5,7)
25/   Cestrum nocturnum, _____ jasmine (3)
26/   Gasteria verrucosa (2,6)
28/   Cordyline terminalis, _____ tree (2)
29/   Polystichum simense (holly fern) (4)
30/   Indoor bulb (4)
32/   Type of succulent (5)
34/   Ctenanthe openheimiana tricolour (5,5,5)
37/   Most common house plant (6)
39/   Aspidistra elatior (4,4,5)
42/   Rosette forming succulents (8)
43/   Eucalyptus globulus (8)
44/   Common house plant (5)

DOWN

2/ Medinilla (4,5)
3/ B. feastii (9,7)
4/ _____ camara (yellow sage) (7)
5/ _____ trifasiata, snake plant (11)
6/ Partridge breasted _____ (common house plant) (4)
7/ The olive (4)
8/ Catharanthus roseus (10,10)
9/ Ribbon plant (8,10)
12/ Lace aloe (4,8)
13/ Aluminium plant (genus) (5)
15/ Popular orchid species (7)
17/ Euphorbia fulgens (7,5)
18/ _____ glabra aka clog plant (9)
19/ Bertolonia marmorata, the _____ plant (5)
21/ Plant of the genus Astrophytum (6)
24/ _____ coccinea (flame of the woods) (5)
27/ Excellent Bonsai genus (4)
31/ Chrysalidolarpus lutescens ___ palm (5)
35/ Fittonia, the _____ plant (3)
36/ Cyrtomium falcatum rochfordianum, the _____ fern (5)
38/ Hang this on your door (5)
39/ Hypocyrta glabra, the _____ plant (4)
40/ Hibiscus is known as the ___ of china (4)
41/ _____ flower (Episcia dianthiflora) (4)

HOUSEPLANTS CROSSWORD #5

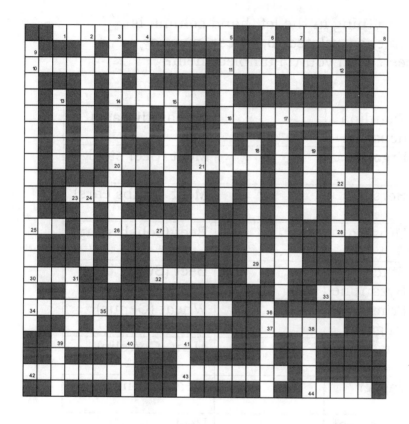

27. WHEAT, MEAT OR BEET

Everything in the left hand column is somehow related to, wheat, meat or beet. Can you unjumbled them?

Fistulina hepatica		Wheat (disease)
Ergot		Meat (Beef steak)
Borscht		Meat (lambs ears)
Drosera		Beet (polish soup)
Stachys Byzantine		Beet (Sugar beet)
Primula vulgaris		Wheat (Genus)
Sugar		Meat (Cowslip)
Jagger		Meat (eating)
Goosefoot		Beet (Chenopodiaceae)
Triticum		Wheat (very common variety)

28. GROUPS AND ROSES

Put these well known roses in there proper groups.

Max Graf		Climbers
Rhapsody in Blue		Ramblers
Pauls scarlet		Floribundas
Dublin bay		Hybrid tea
The fairy		Bourbon
Alec's Red		Shrub
Flower Carpet		Floribunda
Marchesa Boccella		Polyantha
Fantin-Latour		Musks
Dundee rambler		Rugosa
Gertrude Jekyll		Moss
Gloire Lyonnaise		China
Madam Pierre Oger		Species
Madame Delaroche Lambert		Damask
Moonlight		English
Roserie de L'Hay		Alba
Pimpinellifolia		Centifolia
Buff Beauty		Hybrid perpetual
Hermosa		Ground cover
Konigin von Danemark		Ayrshire

29. GARDENING ACROSS THE WORLD

1. Who were the first to carry out grafing?

2. What plant was the first to be grafted by Europeans?

3. What country rescued the French wine industry?

4. Panama disease is a serious fungal disease of which commercial crop?

5. Where did the great potato famine caused by Phytophera infestans oringinate?

6. What is the oldest recorded plant from fossils?

7. Who's the world's largest producer of liquorice?

8. Anigozanthos comes from which country?

9. What is the most widely grown plant in the world?

10. What was the favourite fruit of the ancient Egyptians?

30. SHRUB CROSSWORD #6

ACROSS

1/   Arctostaphylos (9)
3/   Ligustrum (6)
5/   Pyracantha (9)
8/   Winged seed (6)
9/   and 31, Romneya (4,5)
12/   see 21
13/   see 22
15/   Eucryphia (5,4)
16/   and 15 down, Trachelospermum (4,7)
21/   and 12, Garrya (4,6,4)
23/ and 13, Exochorda (5,4)
24/   Perovskia aka
      Russian ___ (4)
25/   See 10 down
28/   and 20 down,
      Physocarpus (4,4)
29/   Dorycnium (6,6)
30/   and 27 down, Grevilla (6,6)
31/   See 9
32/   Aristolichia (12)
33/   ___ broom (spartium) (7)

DOWN

1/ Staphylea (7,3)
2/ Decaisnea, dead mans fingers (4,4)
4/ Hypericum calycinum (4,2,6)
6/ Daboecia (5,5)
7/ Rubus (10,7)
10/ and 25 across, Sarccococa (9,3)
11/ Fremontodendron (7,6)
12/ see 21 across
15/ see 16 across
17/ Gaultheria (11)
18/ Fothergilla (5,5)
19/ Embothrium (7, 4, 5)
20/ see 28 across
22/ Hippophae (12)
21/ Euonymus (12)
26/ Prostanthera rotundifolia,
Australian ____ ____ (4,4)
27/ See 30 across

"Here are sweet peas, on tiptoe for a flight"

Keats

SHRUB CROSSWORD #6

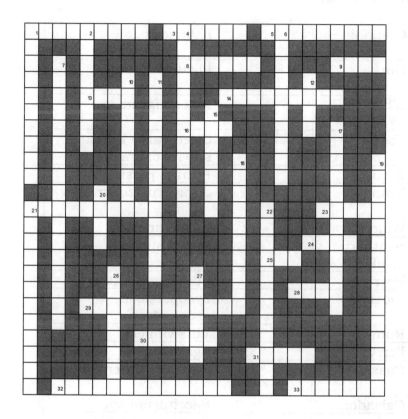

31. THE ALCOHOLIC GARDEN

Match the plant from which the alcohol
is produced.

Grenadine		Palmae sp.
Gin		Illicuim verum
Whisky		Ribes nigrum
Vodka		Sclerocarya birrea subsp. caffra
Tequilla		Prunus persica
Brandy		Juniperus communis
Wine		Hordeum spp.
Southern comfort		Malus sp.
Beer		Punica granatum
Cider		Lycopersicon esculentum
Rum		Vitis vinifera
Perry		Agave sp.
Cassis		Solanum tuberosum
Calvados		Sacchurum spp.
Arak		Pyrus communis
Ouzo		Vitis vinifera
Cointreau		Prunus amygdalus
Amaretto		Humulus lupulus
Amarula		Malus sp.
Bloody Mary		Citrus aurantium

32. DOWN THE ALLOTMENT

Unjumble these well know allotment crops.

WORDJUMBLE
Rjsauecmreleohakit (9,9)
Uaegnbrie (9)
Walfceouilr (11)
Pyecpneaprene (7,6)
Siehelvsecnea (7,6)
Tugoercte (9)
Oensvliongeratni (11,5)
Eoefnenllrcfne (8,6)
Yprbshealgumar (7,7)
Herosdihras (11)
Eyinkbadne (6,4)
Slaichlninhrneopsic (12,7)
Ntateumog (9)
Rwtaaoaemprf (9,3)
Pnbhgnaecnoijsninaeuo (8,8,5)
Lpeubirogocupnrprtclsio (6,9,8)
Hbrbaur (7)
Rnatnrceueslr (7,6)
Obvcasabayge (5,7)
Ereppwtpsee (5,6)
Tfekteaaetmbsoo (9,6)
Esetrsacwr (10)
Trcueabtbn (10)
Eopwotstaet (5,6)
Rueucmeocurhebgnse (10,8)
Dfgsasnrlyie (5,7)

33. MEGAQUIZ # 2

1. Cucumbers and melons are related, true or false?

2. Ikebana is the Japanese art of what?

3. Marine sponge is a plant, true or false?

4. What is kelp?

5. What does Spinescent mean?

6. Which vegetable is found in Moussaka?

7. Gramineous describes which group of plants?

8. Which common fruits belong to the genus Fragaria?

9. The Egyptian water lily is also known as the Lotus, true or false?

10. What is a trug?

11. The common name for Kniphofia is the Jeruselem Sage, true or false?

12. Which plant used to feature on the back of the Three-penny bit?

13. To which Genus does Papyrus belong?

14. To which family does garlic belong?

15. When the stems of plants e.g. Forsythia become flattened, what is it called?

16. What is the latin name for honey fungus?

17. To which genus does gorse belong?

18. Why would you use a soil auger?

19. 10°C converts to how many degrees farenheit

20. Ranunculus belongs to the buttercup family, true or false?

21. What leaf is shown on the Canadian flag?

22. What country has a full grown tree on its national flag?

23. Which plant does the drug digitalin come from and is used for heart conditions?

24. The dried berries of Piper nigra are more commonly known as which condiment?

25. Allspice is the dried berry of which plant?

26. What is an Alligator pear?

27. From which plant is the blue dye "Woad" obtained?

28. A plant that grows high on mountains above the tree line (14,000ft approx.) is described as?

29. Who was the founding father of plant genetics?

30. The botanist Dr. Gaulthier came from which country?

31. From which plant is Henna obtained?

32. To which genus does snakeweed belong?

33. What does polyphyllous mean?

34. Xylem is what part of a plant?

35. Cassia is a course kind of which spice?

36. In botany what does the term parviflorus mean?

37. To which type of flower do we apply the term plenus?

38. To which family does dock belong?

39. If a plant is littoralis where will it grow beside?

40. A plant that is procumbent grows in what manner?

41. To what does the word Sylvan pertain?

42. What is a Taxetum?

43. If a plant is apetalous what is it lacking?

44. What is the term used to describe fan shaped leaves?

45. How do we better know equisetum?

46. What name do we give to the fruit of the rose?

47. To which group of plants does the Venus fly trap belong?

48. Corydalis lutea is what colour?

49. Gutta-percha is a tree product used in the medical profession and the sports industry. Can you name which ones and how is it used?

50. The thickening agent agar used in ice cream making is obtained from which plant?

51. What is unusual about the seeds of a strawberry?

52. From which tree is quinine obtained?

53. These roses have a common acclaim: Felicia, Nozomi, Rosy cushion, Mountbatten. What is it?

54. For which purpose would you use the parasitic wasp Encarsia Formosa?

55. What is the latin name for Witch Hazel?

56. Attar is an extract used in perfumery. What plant is it obtained from?

57. Which fruit is known as the love apple?

58. What would you do with a Howard Gem?

59. What genus of plants is the only one with naturally occurring holes in their leaves?

60. Why would you tine your lawn?

34. THE HEALING GARDEN

1. What plants were used to make aspirin from?

2. Oil of cloves is used to treat which malady?

3. St. Johns Wort is used for the treatment of depression, what is its Latin name?

4. Chamomile is used by young mothers for the relief of what complaint?

5. Which essential oil promotes restful sleep?

6. What plant would you put in a pillow to aid sleep?

7. What would you use an infusion of house leeks for?

8. What primrose is good for pain relief?

9. What is known as the "Wonderous healing plant"?

10. What plant commonly found in the bogs of the Shetland Islands was exported in large quantities to the front lines in WW1 and why?

35. CAN YOU GET RID OF THESE MOLES

1. Moles have necks? True or False

2. The skin on the underside of a mole is extra thin? True or False

3. Moles can see? True or False

4. Moles make nests? True or False

5. Moles only run forwards? True or False

6. Moles never leave their runs? True or False

7. Moles eat mice? True or False

8. Moles only give birth to 1 offspring? True or False

9. Moles hibernate during the winter? True or False

10. Moles can swim? True or False

"Fine words butter no parsnips"

Scott

36. TREE AND SHRUB HEADSCRATCHER

Starting from the top left hand corner, and working clockwise, can you find these plants?

1. Acer (8,5)

2. Ulmus procera (7,3)

3. Philadelphus (4,7)

4. Spanish gorse (7,9)

5. Cordyline australis (7,4)

6. Tsuga canadensis (7,7)

7. Salix caprea pendula (10,6)

8. Pinus strobus "Nana" (8,4)

9. Sambucus (5)

10. Heather (5)

11. Indian bean (7)

12. Shade loving evergreen (11)

13. Danae (11,6)

14. Sweet gum (11)

15. Berberis (8)

16. Taxus (3)

17. Rubus cockburnianus (11,7)
18. Oleaster (9)
19. Clethra (11)
20. Common yew (5,7)
21. Snowy mespilus (11)
22. Rosemary (10)
23. Castanea (5,8)
24. Arbo-vitea (5)
25. Hamamelis japonica (8,5,5)
26. Bourtree (5)
27. Hypericum calycinum (4,2,6)
28. Picea abies (6,6)
29. Hardy plumbago (12)
30. Fraxinus (3)
31. Sea buckthorn (9,10)
32. Coastal shrub (10)
33. Dwarf bamboo (11,13)
34. Swamp cypress (8,9)
35. Dawn redwood (11,16)
36. Hypericum (2,5,4)
37. Quercus with mossy acorn cups (6,3)

38. Jews mallow (6)

39. Horse chestnut (8,13)

40. Araucaria araucana (6,6)

41. Bush clover (9)

42. Snake bark maple (4,13)

43. Polygonum baldschuanicum (4,1,6,4)

44. Pearl bush (9)

45. Olearia (5,4)

46. Potentilla (7,10)

47. Yellow berried holly (4,10,10)

48. Dutchmans pipe (12)

49. Tree of heaven (9,8)

50. Fraxinus ornus (5,3)

51. Chinese witch hazel (9,6)

52. Sorbus intermedia (7,9)

53. Tilia americana (8,4)

54. Quercus robur (7,4)

"How splendid in the morning glows the
lily, with what grace he throws
His supplication to the rose"

Flecker

TREE AND SHRUB
HEADSCRATCHER

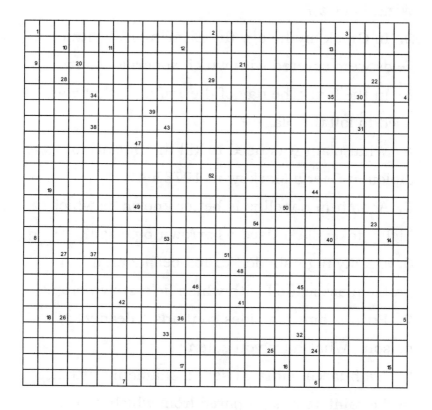

37. SOME DEADLY ONES

1. What was the deadly plant in the film "The Wizard of Oz"?

2. In Greek mythology the Elysian or Elysium fields were covered with which soporific plant?

3. In the film "The day of the Triffids" what was used to kill the plants?

4. What plant was used to kill the Bulgarian diplomat Georgi Markow in 1978?

5. Aconitum napellus is better known as which highly toxic plant used as arrow tip poison?

6. Deadly nightshade (Atropa belladonna) is a problem associated with which field grown crop?

7. Prunus amygdaloides contains a deadly poison. What have you eaten?

8. Ayahuasca, a drug used in shamanic rituals in the rainforest is prepared from which plant?

9. You can eat the leaf stalks but daren't eat the leaf blades, what plant are we referring to?

10. $C_{17}H_{19}NO_3 + H_2O$ is obtained from what common herbaceous border plant?

38. FAIR WEATHER GARDENING

1. What bean causes the most wind?

2. What would you expect with a red sky at night?

3. What is the weather tree and why?

4. Why are marigolds popular as bedding plants?

5. The scarlet pimpernel (Anagallis arvenis) is said to predict the weather. How?

6. If bees stay close to their hive, what should you expect?

7. According to country lore, if onion skins are thick and tough what is it foretelling?

8. Trees can predict when spring has arrived, can you name a well know species that indicates when winter is over and spring has arrived?

9. Why did the ancient Greeks call the wood anemone the wind flower?

10. Why is snow regarded as being a good fertiliser?

39. COMMON TEASERS

Join up the common names for these
well know garden plants

Iris	Aconite
Travellers joy	Michaelmas daisy
Pink	Orchard grass
Goutweed	Clematis
Aster	Ground elder
Cocksfoot	Carnation
Oxlip	Gladdon
Eglantine	Clover
Alsike	Turpintine plant
Goldenrod	Scilla
Squill	Town Hall Clock
Rose of china	Pigweed
Arum	Clematis
Compassplant	Catbriar

COMMON TEASERS contd.

Bistort	Saxifrage
Jack by the hedge	Snakeroot
Greenbriar	Solidago
London Pride	Garlic mustard
Moschatel	Primula
Goosefoot	Hibiscus
Morning glory	Sweetbriar
Old mans beard	Cuckoopint
Mullein	Goosegrass
Twitch	Verbena
Lords and ladies	Honesty
Cinquefoil	Aarons rod
Monkshood	Potentilla
Lunaria	Couch grass
Vervain	Arum
Cleavers	Moon flower

40. TOOLS

1. When using an Averruncator what would you be doing?

2. This tool is derived from the old Adze used in olden times to make boats. Now used to break hard soil pans and grub up tree roots. What is its name?

3. What do you dig up with a Spalding spade?

4. A flat tined fork is used to dig up what vegetables and why is it flat?

5. Mauls are good for laying what in the garden?

6. Wooden billets are used for what purpose?

7. The billhook, used to lay hedges is derived from what weapon of war?

8. What is the difference between a Yorkshire and a Norfolk billhook?

9. What is a Grecian saw?

10. Why would you use a monkey strainer?

41. PERENNIALS AND ANNUALS CROSSWORD #8

ACROSS

3/ And 29 down, Chilean Glory flower (13, 6)

6/ Bamboo (11)

7/ See 31

8/ And 28, Gleditsia triancanthos (5,6)

9/ Morning glory (7)

11/ And 2 down, Sweet allysum (8,8)

12/ See 33

14/ See 21

15/ Rhizomatus perennial (7)

17/ Lady's mantle (10, 6)

20/ French marigold (7)

21/ And 14, Sempervivum (3, 5)

22/ Pansy (5)

23/ _____ strumosa, colourful annual (7)

26/ Silver Cup, Mont Blanc, Ruby Regis are varieties of which plant (8)

28/ See 8

30/ Chelone obliqua (10)

31/ And 7, Tricyrtis nana (4, 4)

32/ See 13 down

33/ And 12 across, hard fern (8, 7)

34/ Muriel bamboo (14, 8)

DOWN

1/ _____ sensibilis (Sensitive fern), (7)

2/ See 11 across

4/ Flea bane (8)

5/ Oxeye daisy (12, 7)

6/ Columbine (9)

10/ Purple moor grass (7, 8)

13/ And 32 across, Nolana paradoxa (7, 10)

16/ Cushion fan flower (8)

18/ And 19, sweet pea (8, 8)

19/ See 18

24/ Penny cress (7)

25/ Buzy lizzies (9)

27/ Popular bedding plant (8)

29/ See 3 across

PERENNIALS AND ANNUALS
CROSSWORD #8

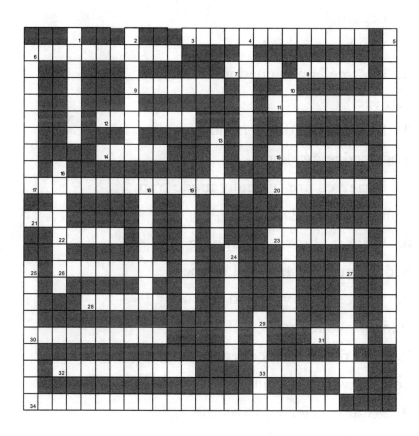

42. KNOW YOUR LIMITS

1. What maple do we commonly use for hedging?

2. What is a fedge?

3. If a tree is pleached what would you see?

4. Dunnock is the common for what hedge dweller?

5. Parterres are typically made from what hedging plant?

6. What is the art of clipping hedges into ornamental shapes?

7. What would you find in the "Alchoholic hedge"?

8. Why do beech hedges retain their dead leaves in the winter?

9. What is referred to as the neighbour from hell?

10. Why should you prune your hedges when they are wet?

43. POND LIFE

1. How many fish per square meter of surface area should you keep in your pond?

2. Pond syndrome refers to what problem?

3. What is the recommended depth that a garden pond should be?

4. Marliac is famous for breeding what type of pond plants?

5. From which country do Koi Carp originate?

6. What type of growing medium should you never put in your pond?

7. Botanically what is a riparian plant?

8. Water lilies are world record holder for what reason?

9. Why is an excess of oxygenating plants detrimental to fish in a pond?

10. What purpose does a UV light have in a modern pond filter?

44. THE BULBOUS JUNGLE

Solve these difficult word jumbles to reveal these bulbous plants.

WORDJUMBLES
Enmnaeo (7)
Pdlsoeah (8)
Dhidgchenatbiyn (7,8)
Aioxhnocod (10)
Ciomrsaco (9)
Lvamnlaaolijicaras (11,7)
Wpaomirirlcne (5,8)
Rnudulcusas (11)
Blbghelnsuleile (7,8)
Aosliugdl (9)
Parietmhpsu (11)
Anhlyaiehctl (12)
Plyodlerllai (7,4)
Ixiloalyftl (7,4)
Tairilaelsrlipaifirmi (11,10)
Ihdnonstia (6,4)
Ltsvianuilsgahna (9,7)
Dnianlymoal (7,4)
Srsaiuncs (9)
Rilyevnlpuai (8,4)
Ncuanlrusu (10)
Forcsarcusfno (7,6)
Lorainctcaspslni (6,3-7)
Worpndos (8)
Olywdlsri (5,4)
Ehtitcepcnsaoaeaiazdih (12,10)

45. LATIN VISITORS

Match up these common garden visitors to their Latin names.

Mole	Sciurlus carolinensis
Grey Squirrel	Vulpes vulpes
Rabbit	Talpa europea
Hedgehog	Felis silvestris catus
Badger	Pipestrelleus pipestrelleus
Deer	Oryctolagus cuniculus
Fox	Erithracus rubecula
Robin	Cervus elephas
Bat	Meles meles
Cat	Erinaceus europaeus

46. THE INDOOR GARDENER

1. Sanseveria trifasiata lourentii must be propagated by what method?

2. What's a mother in laws cushion?

3. How is the cast iron plant pollinated?

4. What common houseplant is nearly extinct in the wild?

5. What common flowering houseplant produces the smallest seeds in the world?

6. Monstera deliciosa, the Swiss cheese plant, produces what edible fruit?

7. Odd one out: Maidenhair fern, Rivertonia, Asparagus sprengeri, Asplenium nidus, Platycerium bifurcatum?

8. What should you never do with a ficus plant?

9. Spathiphyllum wallisii is the plant of choice for NASA space stations. Why is that?

10. Why are pots slightly angled?

47. UNDER THE MICROSCOPE

Can you put the correct symbol with these chemical compounds?

Boron	P_2O_5
Copper	NO_2^-
Phosphorus pentoxide	Zn
Magnesium oxide	B
Iron	Mo
Potassium oxide	MgO
Molybdenum	Cu
Zinc	Fe
Manganese	N
Calcium	K_2O
Nitrogen	Mn
Ammonia	NO_3^-
Nitrite	Ca
Nitrate	NH_3

48. FORTY ODD DISCOVERY PLANTFINDER #9

Clues are across, down, diagonal, forwards and backwards

- Abies amazonica compacta
- Aristolchia durior
- Ceanothus burkwoodii
- Cistus corbariensis
- Corylopsis spicata
- Clematis montana
- Nothofagus antartica
- Bladder senna
- Kalmia angustifolia
- Oleaster
- Nyssa
- Mount Etna Broom
- Libocedrus

FORTY ODD DISCOVERY
PLANTFINDER #9 contd.

- Cryptomeria
- Actinidia
- Liquidambar
- Liriodendron
- Fir
- Plane
- Red Oak
- Tillia
- Prunus avium
- Platanus
- Poplar
- Lavandula vera
- Ilex
- Ulmus

FORTY ODD DISCOVERY
PLANTFINDER #9 contd.

- Rowan
- Yucca
- Dicaisnea
- Spartium
- Pyracantha
- Romneya
- Carryopteris
- Magnolia
- Salix
- Taxus
- Indigo
- Choisya
- Hornbeam
- Neillia thibetica
- Fabiana

FORTY ODD DISCOVERY

PLANTFINDER #9 contd.

a	h	k	o	b	l	a	d	d	e	r	s	e	n	n	a	e	c	u	r	p	s	k	p	s	t
y	b	x	e	l	i	s	u	m	l	u	d	d	j	i	l	o	m	p	t	e	n	a	l	p	s
a	r	i	s	t	o	l	o	c	h	i	a	d	u	r	i	o	r	i	r	u	k	l	n	a	a
c	p	a	e	r	i	l	i	c	b	b	b	a	g	y	r	p	f	i	f	p	f	m	t	r	c
r	o	e	h	s	s	t	e	n	g	k	o	y	l	s	i	m	n	d	a	x	c	i	n	t	i
i	p	r	a	c	a	r	e	a	d	l	o	e	a	i	o	u	j	o	a	t	l	a	e	i	t
l	l	x	y	c	a	r	f	a	s	i	p	n	n	r	d	i	u	o	r	i	w	a	i	u	c
m	a	i	p	l	c	m	i	a	r	t	g	m	s	e	e	v	n	w	a	o	e	n	l	m	r
o	r	l	f	e	o	h	u	z	b	y	e	o	n	t	n	a	i	k	r	y	u	g	l	y	a
u	d	a	v	m	c	p	o	s	o	i	u	r	i	p	d	s	p	r	o	s	o	u	i	o	t
n	y	s	s	a	a	i	s	r	n	n	a	i	g	o	r	u	e	u	s	i	n	s	a	k	n
t	d	o	o	t	a	s	a	i	n	r	i	n	r	y	o	n	r	b	m	h	y	t	t	r	a
e	a	l	l	i	a	e	u	h	s	b	o	c	a	r	n	u	i	s	a	s	m	i	h	a	s
t	i	k	q	s	f	x	n	r	t	s	e	h	a	a	y	r	o	u	r	u	u	f	i	b	u
n	l	l	a	m	g	u	u	s	d	n	p	a	s	c	u	p	p	h	i	n	s	o	b	m	g
a	o	r	y	o	b	t	t	s	i	e	a	i	m	g	o	a	l	t	n	a	t	l	e	a	a
b	n	g	s	n	d	r	d	e	r	a	c	c	c	r	a	m	m	o	u	t	a	i	t	d	f
r	g	a	i	t	b	e	e	r	y	u	c	o	a	a	u	t	p	n	s	a	t	a	i	i	o
o	a	c	o	a	b	h	r	j	k	l	m	e	b	r	t	r	s	a	m	l	a	r	c	u	h
o	m	c	h	n	h	m	l	e	h	c	t	u	d	i	y	a	n	e	c	p	l	s	a	q	t
m	a	u	c	a	i	d	i	n	i	t	c	a	y	p	l	p	d	c	d	t	p	t	o	i	o
c	r	y	p	t	o	m	e	r	i	a	r	a	r	e	v	a	l	u	d	n	a	v	a	l	n
x	i	r	a	m	a	t	a	s	i	s	n	e	i	r	a	b	r	o	c	s	u	t	s	i	c

49. COMMON GARDEN CREATURES

Can you match up the jumbled common names to the Latin.

Chrysopa carnea	Bumble bee
Bombus terrestris	Mole
Macrosiphum rosae	Lacewing
Oniscus asellus	Red Admiral
Lasius niger	Hedgehog
Talpa europaea	Robin
Adalia bipunctata	Rose greenfly
Erinaceus europaeus	2 spotted Ladybird
Erithacus rubecula	Woodlice
Vanessa Atlanta	Ant

50. MEGAQUIZ # 3

1. Pineapples grow on trees, true or false?

2. What would you cure with Rumex?

3. What is the largest garden pest in the UK?

4. What's the Latin name for Mother in Laws tongue?

5. What genus of acid loving popular garden shrubs would you be using when drinking tea?

6. What do you get if you cross a Tangerine with a grapefruit?

7. If you add calcium carbonate to the soil what will happen?

8. Juglans regia produces which edible seeds?

9. Is Balsa wood a hard or soft wood?

10. Where do Welsh onions come from?

11. Where were the hanging gardens of Babylon?

12. What's the largest tree in the world?

13. Why would you use chestnut palings?

14. What is the traditional wood used to grown hop bines?

15. In an onion what does the botanical term 'fistulosum' refer to?

16. What does perennation mean?

17. What would you place in a Garnier bin?

18. Why should horses not eat Senicio jacobea?

19. NPK, can you explain?

20. Copper based fungicides are used in seedlings to prevent what problem?

21. Phytopthera ramorum is a major problem in the UK for what reason?

22. What is an Opuntia?

23. Canna indica was once used as a weapon, name it?

24. Who is the father of Plant taxonomy?

25. A James Grieve is a famous Scottish what?

26. Grapes can be dried to produce these 3 articles of commerce?

27. What is the carbon:nitrogen ratio of bark mulch approximately?

28. What will an annual plant not do?

29. Lactuca sativa is a common salad plant, can you name it?

30. What is the home guard famous for in the garden?

31. Odd one out: Turnip, Carrot, Parsnip, Parsley, Celeriac, Chervil?

32. What palm product has been used for centuries for tying in the garden?

33. The vine Ipomoea batatas produces which common vegetable?

34. What is a way of describing loam?

35. What is a spit in the vegetable garden?

36. The Central American climbing plant vanilla is well known from its use in ice cream manufacture, to what family does it belong?

37. Who invented the seed drill?

38. The fleshy outer coating (aril) of nutmeg is what well known spice?

39. How do we know Vespula vulgaris?

40. What is the most widely grown root crop?

41. What would you eat when you have a plate of spears?

42. The plant Ceiba pentandra was used to save lives, how?

43. What part of the Rhubarb plant do you eat?

44. Is Rhubarb fruit or vegetable?

45. What is Osier?

46. Primula denticulata is so called as it resembles a percussionist's tool?

47. Which fruit is used in Gumbo?

48. What did the abbreviation MAFF stand for?

49. Odd one out: Chardonny, Pineau Noir, Cabernet, Riesling, Chasselas Doré, Pinot Grisio?

50. The jam berry Physalis ixocarpa is more commonly known as?

51. Common name please for this fern Platycerum grande?

52. If pillowing occurs on the nursery what is taking place?

53. To the nearest 10th what is pH neutral?

54. The Spanish marmelo or Quince fruit gave its name to what foodstuff?

55. Why do we use a misting unit in the nursery?

56. What application in commercial horticulture has a rose planter?

57. What lives in a Formicary?

58. Odd one out: Walnut, Pistachio, Butternut, Pecan, Macadamia?

59. The Coolibah tree made famous in the Song 'Waltzing Matilda' belongs to which family?

60. If a plant has a 'Retroactive' name what does it refer to?

51. SOME TASTY DISHES

Match the main plant ingredients to these well know recipes.

1. Rubus ideaus, Ribes alpinum, Ribes nigrum and Triticum spp. ?

2. Brassica oleracea var. botrytis, Daucus carrota, Phaseolus vulgaris, Allium cepa?

3. Olea europea, Ocimum basilicum, Allium sativum, Pinus pinea?

4. Avena sativa, Triticum spp., Sorghum, Hordeum vulgare, Vitis vinifera, Prunus amygdaloides, Corylus avellana?

5. Allium sativum, Lycopersicon esculentum, Solanum melongena, Cucurbita pepo melopepo, Capsicum annuum?

SOME TASTY DISHES contd.

6. Persea Americana, Allium cepa, Capsicum annuum, Coriandrum sativum, Lycopersicon esculentum, Citrus aurantifolia, Piper nigra?

7. Cicer arietinum, Sesamum indicum, Citrus limon, Allium sativum, Punica granatum, Olea europea, Capsicum annuum grossum?

8. Solanum tuberosum, Daucus carota, Pisum sativum, Phaseolus vulgaris, Olea europea, Beta vulgaris rubra, Cucumis sativus?

9. Ananas comosus, Saccharum officinarum, Prunus cerasus, Triticum, Vanilla planifolia?

10. Malus pumila, Juglans regia, Apium graveolens dulce or Apium graveolens rapaceum, Lactuca sativa?

52. FRIEND OR FOE

Can you match up the common name to the Latin name and decide whether they are a gardeners friend of foe.

Common name	Latin name
Ladybirds	Brachycaudus schwartzi
Vine weevil	Coccinella septempunctata
Peach aphid	Artioposthia triangulata
Hover flies	Arion hortensis
Cabbage white	Otiorhynchus sulcatus
Bee	Forficula auricularia
Wasp	Syrphus ribesii
Earwig	Pieris brassicaLacewing
Woodlouse	Phytophthora ramorum
Worm	Oniscus asellus
New Zealand flat worm	Leptinotarsa decemlineata

FRIEND OR FOE contd.

Common name	Latin name
Colorado beetle	Nitrogen fixing enzymes
Sudden oak death	Bombus terrestris
Crown gall	Vespula vulgaris
Toad	Lumbriscus terrestris
Nitrogenase	Meta segmentat
Slug	Carabus nemoralis
Lacewing	Bufo bufo
Ground beetle	Chrysoperla carnea
Garden Spider	Agrobacterium tumefaciens

53. MATCH EM UP FOR BEGINNERS #10

Match up these Latin specific epithets to their translations

SPECIFIC EPITHET	DEFINITION
Zebrina	Of the marshes
Rugosa	Striped
Officianalis	Scarlet
Palustris	Wrinkled
Revoluta	Tongueshaped
Mutabilis	Powerful
Imperialis	Changeable
Linguaeform	Green flowered
Repens	Hatchet shaped
Dolabriforme	Very slender
Cordata	Of herbal shops
Jubatum	Of spring
Cochinea	Three leaved
Graminae	Rock inhabiting
Lacustris	Creeping
Viridiflora	Gleeming
Vernum	Grassy
Pomerdianum	Jawshaped
Trifoliata	Butterfly flowered
Pseudo	Rolled back
Papilio	False
Lupina	Found in lakes
Rubicola	Wolf like
Gracillima	Heart shaped
Fulgens	Post meridian
Maxillare	Crested/maned

54. KEEPING IN SHAPE

Match up the botanical names to
their correct definitions.

Digitate	Spear
Lanceolate	Arrow
Lobata	Needle
Cordate	Lance
Orbicular	Spoon
Rhomboidal	Linear
Sagittate	Scalloped
Hastate	5 Fingered
Deltoid	Toothed
Dentate	Round
Reniform	Lobed
Ensiform	Heart
Filiform	Fan
Pectinate	Triangular
Acicular	Strap
Spathulate	Diamond
Crenate	Comb
Undulate	Kidney
Flabellate	Pointed
Apiculatum	Wavy

55. GARDEN REGULARS (Animals)

Match the common names to these garden regulars

LOCAL NAME	COMMON NAME
MINERS DOG	SHREW
COTTON TAIL	BADGER
THREE COLOUR MOUSE	HEDGE SPARROW
DOWDY COWS	MOLE
HEDGE PIG	EGGPLANT
BROCK	WOOD PIGEON
CUSHET	HEDGEHOG
HALCYON	LADYBIRDS
DUNNOCK	RABBIT
MAD APPLE	KINGFISHER

56. COLLECTIVE NOUNS

Match the collective nouns for these
garden regulars

COLONY	PIGEONS
SWARM	ROOKS
FLIGHT	TURTLEDOVES
ARMY	BEES
CLOWDER	ANTS
SKULK	MAGPIES
CLOUD	CATERPILLARS
HORDE	CATS
ARRAY	FOXES
TIDING	GOLDFISH
KIT	KNATS
BUILDING	HEDGEHOGS
MURMURATION	GOLDFISH
HOST	BUTTERFLIES
PITYING	SPARROWS
SCHOOL	STARLINGS

"Some nocturnal blackness, mothy and warm
When the hedgehog travels furtively over the
lawn"

Hardy

57. KNOCK THE SPOTS OFF THIS!

Match the name of the ladybird to the number of spots

7 Spotted	*Subcoccinella vigintiquattuorpunctata*
2 Spotted	*Hippodamia tredecimguttata*
10 Spotted	*Coccinella septempunctata*
11 Spotted	*Psyllobora (Thea) vigintiduopunctata*
18 Spotted	*Adalia decempunctata*
22 Spotted	*Tytthaspis (Micraspis) sedecimpunctata*
14 Spotted	*Coccinella quinquepunctata*
16 Spotted	*Propylea quattuordecimpunctata*
24 Spotted	*Coccinella undecimpunctata*
13 Spotted	*Myrrha octodecimguttata*
5 Spotted	*Adalia bipunctata*

58. TREE AND SHRUB MIX EM UP

Rearrange columns 2 and 3 into the correct order as shown below

Acer	japonicum	Aureum

GENUS	SPECIES	CV./VARIETY
Acer	glabra	Variegate
Aucba	baccata	macrobotrys
Berberis	biloba	Aureum
Clematis	japonicum	Plena
Cornus	ottawensis	Plenus
Deutzia	japonicum	Purpurea
Euonymus	alba	Radiacans
Fraxinus	japonica	Meyeri
Ginkgo	orientalis	Bluebird
Hydrangea	nitida	Sibirica
Ilex	fortunei	Charles x

TREE AND SHRUB MIX EM UP

GENUS	SPECIES	CV./VARIETY
Juniperus	excelsior	Faastigiata
Kerria	scabra	Rubra
Lonicera	officianalis	Pendula
Magnolia	squamata	Albus
Picea	aria	Baggesensgold
Prunus	triloba	Bassiflava
Rhus	aquifolium	Cole
Rosmarianus	canadensis	Multiplex
Salix	soulangeana	Kosta
Sorbus	serrata	Laciniata
Syringa	europaeus	Pleniflora
Taxus	pungens	Lutescens
Tsuga	floribunda	Chermesina
Ulex	vulgaris	Orangepeel
Wisteria	alba	Ellegantissima

59. CLIMBING UP THE WALL

1. Eccremocarpus scaber the colourful garden climber originates from which part of the world?

2. When do you prune 'Group 1' Clematis?

3. What does a rose use to climb?

4. Spell Wisteria?

5. Can you give the Latin name for the mile a minute plant?

6. What county in England grows the most hops?

7. What do you call a field of hops?

8. Why should you train your climbing roses horizontally?

9. What could you eat if you grow an Actinidia chinensis up your wall?

10. The flowers of which climber are dried in an Oast House?

60. DO YOU KNOW YOU APPLES

All of the apples below are either Desert, cookers or cider apples, can you decide which?

Cox's orange pippin	
Lane's Prince Albert	
Bramley's seedling	
Newton wonder	
Red Soldier	
Laxton's superb	
Charles Ross	
American mother	
Grenedier	
Sweet coppin	
Worcester permain	
Blenheim Orange	
Granny smith	
Egremont russet	
Diamond Jubilee	
Tremlitts Bitter	
Reinette de Canada	
James Grieve	
Kingston black	
Court Pendu Plat	

61. ON THE FUCHSIA TRIAL

Can you place these Fuchsia's into their correct groups: **BUSH, CLUSTER OR TRAILING**

Avocet	Bush
Triphylla	Cluster
Cascade	Trailing
Alice Hoffman	Bush
Marinka	Trailing
Ting-a-Ling	Bush
Mission Bells	Bush
Pink Galore	Trailing
Rufus the Red	Bush
Thalia	Cluster
Winston Churchill	Bush
Swingtime	Trailing
Summer Snow	Trailing
Golden Treasure	Bush
Flash	Cluster
Sunray	Bush
Tom Thumb	Bush
Tom West	Trailing
Mrs Popple	Bush
Auntie Jinks	Trailing

62. BLUE FOR YOU

Can you match up these blue flowering plants?

Cyananthus microphyllus	Trailing bell flower
Gentiana farreri	Gentian
Lithospermum oleifolium	Gromwell
Primula marginata 'Linda Pope'	Rockery Primrose
Veronica rupestris	Rockery Speedwell
Campanula calycanthema	Canterbury Bells
Cobaea scandens	Cathedral Bell
Convolvulus 'Royal Ensign'	Morning Glory
Nemophila menziesii	Baby Blue Eyes
Myosotis alpestris	Forget me not
Nigella damascene 'Miss Jeckyll'	Love in a Mist
Agapanthus campulatus 'Isis'	African Lilly
Aconitum 'Sparks Variety'	Monkshood

BLUE FOR YOU contd.

Anchusa 'Dropmore'	Alkanet
Catananche caerulea	Cupids Dart
Echinops ritro	Globe Thistle
Omphalodes cappadocica	Naval Wort
Platycodon grandiflorum mariesii	Balloon Flower
Polemonium caeruleum	Jacobs Ladder
Veronica gentianoides	Speedwell

"Mid hush'd, cool-rooted flowers, fragrant-eyed, blue, silver-white, and budded Tyrian"

Keats

63. THE NAMES THE SAME

All these plants have connections to the animal kingdom, can you name them?

Tacca	
Mentha	
Beloperone gutta	
Primula veris	
Mimulus	
Erigeron	
Cardamine	
Aruncus	
Strelitzia reginae	
Linaria	
Auricaria auracana	
Quercus cerris	
Clemone spinosa	
Coreopsis	
Lychnis	
Delphinium	
Acanthus	
Cimicifuga	
Antennaria	
Doronicum	
Eremurus	

64. CAN YOU SEE A RAINBOW

There is a colour in each of these trees and shrubs common name, can you find them?

Sequoia sempervirens	
Sorbus aria	
Betula pendula	
Fagus sylvatica	
Eucalyptus globules	
Gaultheria	
Laburnum	
Populus alba	
Prunus spinosa	
Tillia cordata	
Caryopteris	
Choisya	
Decaisnea fargesii	
Halesia	
Indigofera	
Philadelphus	
Syringa	
Santolina	
Abies	
Cedrus atlantica glauca	

65. IN AND AROUND THE POND

All these plants are either deep water, floaters, oxygenators, marginals or bog plants. Can you give them their common names and their preffered habitat?

Aponogeton	
Lemna	
Fontinalis	
Acorus	
Trollius	
Nymphoides	
Glyceria	
Lagarosiphon	
Urticularia	
Orontium	
Polygonum	
Hydrocharis	
Potamogeton	
Lysichiton	
Cotula	
Elodea	
Nuphar	
Stratiotes	
Onoclea	
Menyanthus	

66. FOOD FOR FREE

All these edible plants can be found in and around the field hedgerows, can you match the Latin to there more familiar names?

Sloe		Rubus fruiticosus
Green Gage		Sambucus nigra
Damson		Prunus spinosa
Field mushroom		Prunus italica
Blackberry		Prunus damascena
Alexanders		Agaricus campestris
Elderberry		Alliaria petiolata
Horseradish		Corylus avellana
Marsh Samphire		Urtica dioica
Hop		Smrynium olusatium
Nettle		Humulus lupulus
Hazelnut		Salicornia europea
Crab apple		Rumex acetosa
Wild garlic		Armoracia rusticana
Black walnut		Malus sylvestris
Dandeloin		Langermannia gigantean
Wild raspberry		Mespilus germanica
Sorrel		Juglans nigra
Medlar		Taraxacum officinale
Giant puff ball		Rubus idaeus

67. NUTS ABOUT NUTS

Can you match the common nut name
to the Latin botanical name?

Nutmeg	Arachis hypogea
Hazelnut	Macadamia turnifolia
Almond	Juglans nigra
Shea nut	Corylus avelana
Peanut	Prunus amygdalus
Pine nut	Castanea sativa
Cashew	Pinus spp.
Macadamia	Pistacia vera
Coconut	Carya illinoensis
Pistachio	Anacardium occidentale
Sweet Chestnut	Coccus nucifera
Heart nut	Simmondsia chinensis
Bread nut	Bertholletia excelsa
Pecan	Juglans sieboldiana
Walnut	Elaeis guinneensis
Beech nut	Parkia Africana
Goat nut	Butyrospermum parki
Brazil nut	Ophiocaryon paradoxum
Snake nut	Brosimum alicastrum
Palm nut	Fagus sylvatica

68. MEGA STATE TO BE IN

All of the United states have a state flower. Can you unjumble and match them up?

Alabama		Purple Violet
Arkansas		Hawthorn
Conneticut		Purple Lilac
Delamare		Blue Bonnet
Florida		Golden Rod
Georgia		Rose
Kentucky		Magnolia
Louisiana		Flowering Dogwood
Maine		Mistletoe
Maryland		Mountain Laurel
Massachusetts		Violet
Mississippi		Carolina jessamine
New Hampshire		Camellia
New Jersey		Apple blossom
New York		Mountain Laurel
North Carolina		Peach Blossom
Oklahoma		Thunbergia
Pennsylvania		Arbutus
Rhode Island		Orange Blossom
South Carolina		Cherokee Rose
Tennessee		Goldenrod
Texas		Magnolia
Vermont		Tassle
Virginia		Rhododendron
West Virginia		Apple Blossom
Illinois		Red Clover

MEGA STATE TO BE IN contd.

Indiana		Native Violet
Iowa		Scarlet Carnation
Kansas		Flowering Dogwood
Michigan		Peony
Minnesota		American Pasque Flower
Missouri		Oregon Grape
Nebraska		Golden Poppy
North Dakota		Bitter Root
Ohio		Wild Rose
South Dakota		Syringa
Wisconsin		Sunflower
Alaska		Sage Brush
Arizona		Iris
California		Wild Prairie Rose
Colorado		Saguaro
Hawaii		Pink and White Lady's Slipper
Idaho		Sego Lily
Montana		Coast Rhododendron
Nevada		Indian Paintbrush
New Mexico		Rocky Mountain Columbine
Oregon		Yucca
Utah		Hibiscus
Washington		Wood Violet
Wyoming		Forget-me-not

69. MUSICAL CRYPTIC PLANTS

These cryptic clues will lead to the names of well known popular groups or musicians. Can you name them?

1. You'll need plenty to drink after hearing this band?
2. Pistols and plants?
3. We'll need Triticum to get this group?
4. Nutty hedgerow, punk before Des?
5. When you go to the toilet don't forget a good book?
6. The song remains the same for this front man?
7. This band is a festive favourite?
8. The tide is out for this American band?
9. Bouganvillea's maybe?
10. Bean fighting again have you?

"Here's flowers for you,
Hot Lavender, mints, savory, marjoram,
The marigold, that goes to bed wi 'the sun'
And with him rises weeping"

Shakespeare

70. RIPARIAN RASCALS

These plants occur beside water.
Can you match the correct common
against the Latin botanical name?

Latin		Common
Zantedeschia		Water Buttercup
Sparganium		Water Forget-me-not
Veronica		Arrowhead
Typha		Arrow Arum
Ranunculus		Arum
Sagittaria		Reedmace
Peltandra		Bur-Reed
Saururus		Water Mint
Myosotis		Marsh St. Johns Wort
Scirpus		Pickerel Weed
Pontederia		Cotton Grass
Myriophyllum		Brooklime
Mimulus		Umbrella grass
Juncus		Parrots feather
Mentha		Lizards Tail
Hypericum		Monkey Flower
Eriophorum		Sedge
Cyperus		Bullrush
Carex		Marsh Marigold
Caltha		Rush

71. GET BUSY WITH THE BEES

1. Bees collect two food items, can you name them?
2. For what does the bee keeper use the term bee bread?
3. The time of year when honey making is in full production is known as?
4. There are 3 kinds of bee in the working hive can you name them?
5. To what genus do bees belong?
6. How is bees wax formed?
7. The word swarm is of German origin, what does it mean?
8. How is the bee hive cooled in very hot weather?
9. The bees store the honey in an intricate collection of chambers, can you name them, what there made from and how many sides has each chamber?
10. How many eggs will the queen lay in a day?
11. Bees collect a gummy substance from trees such as horse chestnut. It is used to fill cracks and block drafts in the hive, can you name it?

12. What bearing do blue and great tits have on bees?
13. What plant is the most prolific source of honey production in the UK?
14. Odd one out: Vinegar, raw onion, oil of wintergreen, nutmeg, bluebag?
15. In olden days when bees swarmed beekeepers saw this as a sign of what?
16. What is the correct term for a beekeeper?
17. Which honeybee has the largest brain?
18. A worker bee produces a special type of food when in waiting to the queen can you name it?
19. To develop from the egg to the fully formed queen takes how long?
20. What is unusual about the egg that a drone bee is hatched from?

"There's a whisper down the field where the year has shot her yield
And the ricks stand grey to the sun
Singing over then, come over for the bee has quit the clover
And your English summers done"

Kipling

72. MIND YOU PEAS AND B'S

Can you give the common name of these peas and beans?

Vicia faba	Windsor or broadbean
Phaseolus vulgare	Common American bean
Phaseolus lunatus	Lima or butter bean
Phaseolus aureus	Mung bean
Vigna sinensis	Cow pea
Glycine soja	Soy bean
Dolichos lablab	Bonavist bean
Phaseolus coccineus	Runner bean
Dolichos biflorus	Horsegram bean
Pisum sativum	English pea
Lathyrus odoratus	Sweet pea
Tingitanus	Tangier pea
Carbanzo	Chick pea
Sicer arietinum	Spanish pea
Cajanus indicum	Pigeon pea
Lotus tetragonolobus	Asparagus pea
Canavalia ensiformis	Jack bean
Cyamopsis psoraloides	Cluster bean
Phaseolus mungo	Black gram bean
Canavalia gladiata	Sword bean

73. SOW YOUR SEEDS

Can you give the Latin botanical name for these common edible seeds?

Sunflower	
Poppy	
Sesame	
Pumpkin	
Carroway	
Corriander	
Cumin	
Wheat	
Sweet corn	
Oats	
Fennell	
Musturd	
Cardamom	
Fenugreek	
Black pepper	
Garden pea	
Lentils	
Rice	
Barley	
Peanut	

"Read my little fable
He that runs may read
Most can raise the flowers now
For all have got the seed"   **Tennyson**

74. WILD WHO AM I?

Guess the name of these wild flowering plants from their descriptions?

1. I am a woody climbing plant, I can reach 100 feet, I have long plumed seeds, my names include Old man's beard and boys bacca. My latin name is Clematis Vitalba. Who am I?

2. The Roman Goddess of corn (Ceres) wore a wreath made from my bretheren, I was widespread before selective herbicides, once upon a time I was used medicinally, my bright red flowers can be seen on rememberance day. Papaver rhoeas is my Latin title. Who am I?

3. Amongst my common names are runch, cadlock and charlock, I will invade any arable land, my flowers are white lilac or yellow, left alone I will produce 2 inch seed pods, my latin name is Raphanus raphanistrum. Who am I?

4. Capsella bursa-pastoris is my true name, I am a self pollinator, I am also known as scrip and mothers heart, perhaps I would be of use to the sheep farmer. Who am I?

5. In Yorkshire I am known as Tang-Tong, my true name is Nasturtium officinale, I am rich in vitamin C and have a peppery taste, though I should not be eaten when found in still water. Who am I?

6. I am a lover of rich soils but can grow anywhere, Silenus the woodland god gave me my Latin name, my red flowers are single sexed and I can reach 36 inches in height. Who am I?

7. I have been called thunderflower and batchelors buttons, my flowers are bright pink and are seen in damp woodland, marshes and water meadows, my latin name means Cuckoo – flower. Who am I?

8. My Latin means little star, I can flower all through the year, I am hated by every gardener, cage birds have a fondness for me though I can be eaten by humans. Who am I?

9. I will answer to Sally-my-handsome, though my true name is Carpobrotus edulis, I belong to the mesembryanthemum family, my flowers open when sunny and close when gloomy, my flowers are magenta or yellow and I am vistor from South Africa. Who am I?

10. My three lobed leaflets fold down at night, and my common names are sleeping beuty and sleeping clover, I am very acid to the taste. Who am I?

11. Because of the shape of my lower sepals they call me policemans helmet, I was introduced in 1839 from Asia. Who am I?

12. Also known as Crows-toes, God almightys thumb and finger and ladys shoes and stockings and bacon and eggs, the green hair streak butterfly chooses me to lay her eggs upon, botanically I am Lotus corniculatus. Who am I?

13. I was once used to flavour mead, I have been used in medicine as I contain pain killing ingredients similar to Salicylic acid, my common name is courtship and matrimony. Who am I?

14. I am dedicated to the Virgin Mary, alchemists of old collected the early morning dew from my leaves to use in their experiments, I practice guttation during humid times. Who am I?

15. The Tudors thought me the king of vegetables, my leaves have a decidedly sour taste. My leaves turn crimson late in the year and my latin name means to suck vineger. Who am I?

16. I gave my common name to a book about the French revolution, although my name suggests my flowers are red, I also come in various other colours I have also been known as a shepards sundial, change-of-the-weather and the laughter bringer. Who am I?

17. You can see from my nicknames of Satin cherries and devils rhubarb that I am unwanted and every part of me is poisonous. I belong to the potato family. Who am I?

18. I am now protected in the wild but was once used to make glue. I am white or blue. Who am I?

19. Known locally as the moon daisy, dog daisy or marguerite I will flower all summer, in former times I was a medicinal plant and I prefer the rich southern soils. Who am I?

20. One of my oddities is that I only have 2 leaves, I can be found from sand dunes to woods and meadows, I am thought to be the most widespread of British orchids, my flowers are small and green but numerous. Who am I?

75. FILL IN THE BLANKS
GARDEN PROVERBS

1. As is the _____, so is the _____?
2. As a ____ falls, so must it ___?
3. Great ____ from little _____ grow?
4. To be in _____?
5. Better to be stung by a _____, than pricked by a ____?
6. As white as a ____?
7. No ____ without a ____?
8. March ____ and April _____ bring forth May _____?
9. When you can tread on nine _____ at once, _____ has come?
10. Turnips like a dry ___ but a wet ____?
11. This rule in gardening never _____, to sow ___ and to set ___?
12. When the ____ is out of bloom, _____ is out of fashion?
13. Plant ____ for your heirs?
14. If on the ____ the leaves still ____ the coming _____ will be ____?
15. Don't pull your ____ in May wait until another ___?

76. MORE TASTY DISHES

Country	Meat/Veg	Plant Ingredients	Dish
India	Chicken	Zingiber officinale, Allium sativum, Capsicum frutescens, Curcuma longa, Citris limon, Coriandrum sativa	
Morocco	Lamb	Allium cepa, Petroselinum crispum, Coriandrum sativa, Mentha spicata, Cumimum cyminum, Capsicum annuum, Piper nigra	
Mexico	Veg	Phaseolus vulgaris, Allium cepa, Allium sativum, Laurus nobilis, Capsicum frutescens, Zea mays, Lycopersicon esculentum	
Spain	Veg	Capsicum annum, Cucumis sativus, Allium cepa, Capsicum frutescens, Lycopersicon esculentum, Olea europeaus, Piper nigra	
Mexico	Veg	Zea mays	

Greece	Veg	Cicer arietinum, Citris limon, Allium sativum, Olea europeaus, cayenne pepper, tahini, Piper nigra, Petroselinum crispum	
Ireland	Lamb	Allium cepa, Daucus carota, Solanum tuberosum, Thymus spp. , Petroselinum crispum, Piper nigra	
Thailand	Veg	Triticum spp. , Saccharum officinarum, Cocos nucifera, Sesamum indicum, Musa	
Thailand	Veg	Manihot utilissima	
Italy	Veg	Zea mays, Olea europeaus, Allium cepa, Myristica fragrans, Petroselinum crispum, Piper nigra	
Italy	Veg	Allium cepa, Olea europeaus, Triticum spp., Fungi, Petroselinum crispum or Mentha spicata	
Japan	Veg	Raphanus?, Triticum spp., Ipomoea batatas, Daucus carota, shiitake mushroom, Phaseolus vulgarus, Capsicum annum	

ANSWERS

1. THESE TREES ARE A BREEZE

1. The Bristlecone pine (4600 years old)
2. Yew
3. Beech
4. White poplar
5. The conkers were used to make a shin linement for lame horses in Italy
6. Wayfairing tree (Viburnum lantana)
7. Sequoiadendron giganteum
8. Sequoia sempervirens
9. A stand of Aspens in North America
10. Gingko biloba

2. IN THE SHRUBBERY

1. Spindle tree (Euonymus europaeus)
2. Shillelagh
3. David Austin
4. Gorse (Ulex europeaus)
5. Syringa (the others are Ericaceous or Theaceous)
6. Rosemary (Rosmarinus officinalis)
7. Anti clockwise
8. Vitex agnus-castus
9. Cultivated variety
10. Nigella (Love in a mist is a half hardy annual all the others are shrubs)

3. PERENNIAL CHALLENGE

1. Bears foot
2. Red valerian (Centranthus ruber)
3. Used as tobacco substitutes
4. Yarrow (Umbellifereae, others are Asteraceae)
5. Banana (Musa spp.)

3. PERENNIAL CHALLENGE contd.

6. Lamium (Dead nettle)
7. Elwesii (e.g. Galanthus elwesii) others are Iris spp.
8. Flowers open from the top of the flower spike whereas stem flowering plants flowers from the bottom upwards.
9. The pigmentation on the leaves changes colour from yellow to white throughout the growing season.
10. A x Hecharella

4. ANNUAL HORRIBILIS

1. The Victorians
2. Viola
3. In a hanging basket (Creeping Jenny)
4. Limnanthes douglasii
5. Centaurea cineraria
6. Lycopersicum esculentum (Tomato)
7. Annual meadow grass, (Poa annua) a weed grass on golf greens which dies out in drought leaving bare patches
8. Eat them, they are Sweet Peppers
9. Zinnia elagans is the only annual the others being biennials, ephemerals
10. Parsley, is a biennial.

5. GENERAL CROSSWORD #1

6. THE HERB GARDEN

1. Autumn crocus
2. Coriander
3. Basil
4. Contain in a plunged bucket to control its invasive habit
5. Alecost
6. Common parsley

6. THE HERB GARDEN contd.

7. English Gin
8. Bouquet garni
9. Brassicaceae
10. Horseradish

7. VEGETABLE SOUP

1. Potato (the tubers are highly poisonous when green)
2. Carotene (Caretenoids)
3. Garden pea
4. Flower
5. Large pearl
6. James Grieve is an apple the rest are Potatoes
7. Carrots
8. Lilliaceae
9. Brassica bullata
10. Solanaceae (Potato family)

8. FUNGI FINDER

1. Oxyporus nobilissimus (Giant polypore)
2. Otherwise known as the yellowish olive death cap it is the worlds most poisonous fungus.
3. Inocybe patouillardii is the only poisonous one.
4. Eat it! It's the common field mushroom.
5. The piedmont or white truffle.
6. Fire. It is used for tinder as it is easily ignited and smoulders for a long time.
7. Chlorophyll. None of them can make food by photosynthesis
8. The nettle
9. A fungi
10. Fairy rings

PLANT HUNTER	PLANT
Sir Joseph Hooker	Himalayan Birch
Nathanial Wallich	Himalayan White Pine
Englebert Kampher	Gingko biloba
William Kerr	Chinese Juniper
Robert Fortune	Cryptomeria japonica
Grigori Nicolevich Potanin	Chinese larch
John Gould Veitch	Magnolia stellata
George André Soulié	Buddlia
Victor Jacquemont	Doedar cedar
Lady Amherst	Clematis montana

10. UNWANTED GUESTS

1. The oak gall wasp that lay their eggs in oak buds in winter causing the bud to enlarge and become woody and gall like.

2. Bitter pit

3. Mouldy knob

4. Frass is caterpillar excrement and therefore your are likely to see caterpillar damage?

5. Vine weevil

6. The sun. It is a sign of heat injury.

7. Garden slug

8. Dutch Elm Disesase (DED)

9. The potato's were propagated vegetatively rendering them to be highly susceptible due to them all being clones of a parent plant. The disease spread rapidly because of this reason now over come by sexual propagated seed.

10. The common wasp.

11. GENERAL CROSSWORD #2

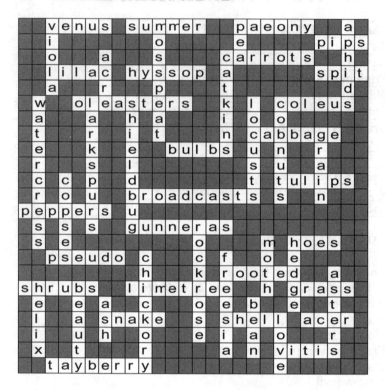

12. WEED THESE OUT

1. Umbelliferae
2. The dock rubbed on the nettle sting
3. Cleavers, bedstraw (Gallium aparine)
4. Horehound is a medicinal herb the rest are common names for Ragwort (Senecio jacobea)
5. Types of thistle
6. Poa annua, annual meadow grass a pernicious grass weed that occurs on fine turf. Seed heads occur below the mower blades and die out in dry weather leaving bare patches.

12. WEED THESE OUT contd.

7. It comes from the French Dent de lion, the lions tooth.

8. Water hyacinth, spreads vigorously in water courses and lakes and blocks them

9. 14 on Trifolium pratense

10. Any plant that crowds out cultivated plants

13. PRICKLY CUSTOMERS

1. Tequilla

2. Alluadia, is the only succulent, the others are cacti.

3. 10-75 years (sorry not 100)

4. Mesembryanthemaceae (the Livingstone daisy family)

5. The cowboy cactus (regarded as being the worlds largest cactus

6. Easter cactus.

7. Your mother in law, commonly known as the Mother in laws cushion

8. The peyote cactus (Lophophora williamsii). A hallucinogenic plant used by the Mexican and Red Indian tribes.

9. Mexican firecracker plant

10. Aloe vera

Gertrude Jekyll	(1843 - 1932)
Humphrey Repton	(1752-1818)
Rosemary Very	(1919-2001)
Sir Joseph Paxton	(1803-1865)
Pliny the elder	(23-79AD)
Carl Linnaeus	(1707-1778)
Vita Sackville-West	(1892-1962)
Brown, Lancelot ('Capability')	(1716-1782)
Tradescant, John	(1608-1662)
Gertrude Jekyll	(1843 - 1932)

15. THE ABUNDANT ORCHID

1. Vannilla
2. Half a millimetre
3. They lure pollinators by mimicking male insects
e.g. bee orchids attract bees who are searching for
mates unknown to them they are flowers and they
unwillingly pollinate them.
4. Trilobite is a fossil of an animal, the others are
types of orchid.
5. They all posses 6 tepals i.e. 3 sepals and 3 petals
6. Is the world's largest orchid. They grow in the
crotches of large trees (Epiphytic). They can attain 5
meters long and weigh 2000kg causing large trees,
upon which they grow, to crash to the ground.
7. 28

15. THE ABUNDANT ORCHID contd.

8. A bottom lip used as a landing zone for insects
9. On the ground
10. The moth orchid, Phalaenopsis.

16. LAWN TO BE PROUD OF

1. To aerate your lawn. A hollow tine is used to extract cores of soil which are filled with top dressing to encourage new grass roots to grow.
2. You have found the larvae of the common Cockchafer or may bug which eats grass roots causing bare patches on your lawn.
3. A dustbin lid. A hole of was removed where the handle sits and a engine was attached with a rotating blade beneath.
4. Edward Beard Budding (also invented the adjustable spanner)
5. Chamomile nobilis (A chamomile lawn)
6. The grass produces new growth from the meristemetic tissue from the base allowing it to be cut short. This is a characteristic of monocotyledonous plant. Dicotlyledonous plants have meristem tissues at the growing tips.
7. 3:1:2 NPK (Therfore removing the grass clippings slows growth down but reduces thatch build up)
8. Iron (Ferrous sulphate)]
9. Worm casts
10. From the French word Laund meaning a plain sprinkled with trees and underbrush, a glade.

17. BULBWORD #3

18. COMPOST BREAKDOWN

1. Orange peel as it contains antibacterial organic compounds from the skins. These destroy benefical microbes which are used to decompose the contents.

2. John Innes Compost

3. Coconut fibre

4. Ericaceous or lime free composts (low pH)

5. Vine weevil larvae

6. 20 times

7. Flowers of sulphur

8. Calcium carbonate (Dolomitic lime also contains magnesium)

9. On the ground to allow worms to enter and moisture to escape and not on a hard surface.

10. They grow in the spaces in soil!

19. PEACH, PLUM OR PEAR

Kieffer	Pear
Rio Oso Gem	Peach
Chickasaw	Plum
Weaver	Plum
Belle of Georgia	Peach
Dixie Red	Peach
Winter Nelis	Pear
Halehaven	Peach
Victoria	Plum
Desoto	Plum
Buerre Hardy	Pear
Reine Claude	Plum
Triogem	Peach
Elberta	Peach
Coyenne du Comice	Pear
Williams	Pear
Lombard	Plum
Bartlet	Pear
Sunhigh	Peach
Anjou	Pear

20. MEGAQUIZ #1

1. Cashew nut
2. Tarragon
3. Food source from the Arum family
4. Aloe
5. Tannin
6. Leaf like appendage at the base of a leaf petiole usually found in pairs.
7. Crowded
8. More than two
9. Gooseberrry
10. Bog myrtle (Myrica gale)
11. Tricarpous

12. Tapering to a point as in many spruce trees.
13. Seed coating
14. Achene
15. The protective discharge from the froghopper insect
16. Level treeless plane found in northern South America
17. Tansy
18. Madagascar
19. Hooked
20. Opium poppy (Papaver somniferum)
21. Wheat
22. Fruitfull
23. Ginger
24. Mast
25. Pandanus (Tropical foliage plants)
26. Ruta
27. A small pear
28. Bearing acorns or other nut like fruits
29. Common Hawthorn?
30. A black hellebore
31. A Mexican bean
32. A hard swelling on the trunk of a tree (Gall)
33. Kohlrabi
34. Viburnum tinus
35. Belonging to the Mallow family
36. A thorny shrub Zizyphus spina-christi
37. Oenothera
38. Pampiniform
39. Quince
40. Tree
41. Whitebeam
42. Turpentine tree
43. Mandrake
44. Manilla hemp
45. Seaweed
46. Small wood
47. Scilla maritime

48. Lilyturf
49. A calyx
50. The nutrient solution in the soil is stronger than that of the plant causing a reversed osmosis
51. Pomegranate
52. Radish
53. Ruby tailed (It's a wasp, the others being species of Bee's)
54. The growing tip bud which show dominance over the lateral buds.
55. Tends to grow tall and thin due to poor lighting conditions and stems and leaves become blanched (loss of chlorophyll)
56. Perrennation
57. Station sowing
58. King shoot
59. Gooseberry
60. Dessert apple

21. FLOWERING PLANTS CROSSWORD #4

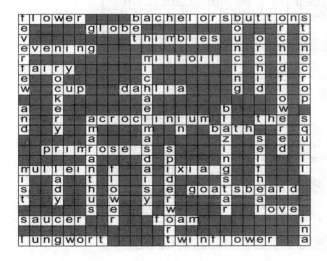

22. INCREASING YOUR STOCK

1. Top part or the ornamental desirable part which is grafted to the rootstock.
2. From seed
3. Gibberellic acid
4. Budding (T budding)
5. Spores (Sporangia)
6. Seed which is sexual, the others are vegetative thus asexual or clonal ie each offspring is an exact gentic clone of the parent material.]
7. Dicotyledonous
8. Callus formation is greater along the wound as a result of increased cambium exposure.
9. In grafting together incompatible woody plants where the scion and rootstock refuse to join
10. Bulbs e.g. Hyacinth, to encourage axil bulbs to develop

23/ FIND 40 FUNGI (CROSSWORD GRID)

24. COLLOQUIALISMS

COUNTY NAME	COUNTY	COMMON NAME
Shiners	East Anglia	Lord and ladies
Skeet plant	Cornwall	Hogweed
Shoes and stockings	Gwent	Birds foot trefoil
Vervine	Manx	Motherwort
Witchen	Worcestershire	Rowan
Minerac	County Offaly	Selfheal
Lady's milk sile	Cheshire	Lungwort
Honey – sookies	Shetland	Lousewort
Everlasting sin	Shropshire	Slender speedwell
Fairies petticoat	Cheshire	Foxglove
Dead mans bells	Morayshire	Sea campion
Black knobs	Peak district	Alder fruits
Ascension	East Anglia	Groundsel
Money in both pockets	Kent	Honesty
Mogue Tobin	County Carlow	Corn marigold
Old mans pepper	Nottinghamshire	Meadowsweet
St John of Beverly	Humberside	Primroses
Tom –bacca	Sussex	Travellers joy
Wavverin leaf	Shetland	Greater plantain
God's hand leaf	Gloucestershire	Valarian

25. CHRISTMAS CRACKER

1. Poinsettia
2. A kiss
3. Yule log
4. Christmas rose
5. Holly and the ivy
6. Christmas tree (Norway spruce)
7. Turkey (Cranberry sauce)
8. Sage and onion stuffing
9. Plum pudding
10. Roast parsnips

26/ HOUSEPLANTS CROSSWORD #5

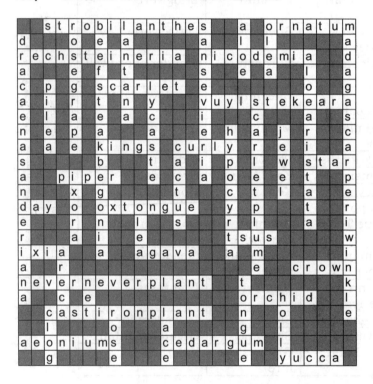

27. WHEAT, MEAT OR BEET

Fistulina hepatica	Meat (Beef steak)
Ergot	Wheat (disease)
Borscht	Beet (polish soup)
Drosera	Meat (eating)
Stachys Byzantine	Meat (lambs ears)
Primula vulgaris	Meat (Cowslip)
Sugar	Beet (Sugar beet)
Jagger	Wheat (very common variety)
Goosefoot	Beet (Chenopodiaceae)
Triticum	Wheat (Genus)

28. GROUPS AND ROSES

Climbers	Dublin bay
Ramblers	Pauls scarlet
Floribundas	Moonlight
Hybrid tea	Alec's Red
Bourbon	Madam Pierre Oger
Shrub	Max Graf
Floribunda	Rhapsody in Blue
Polyantha	The fairy
Musks	Buff Beauty
Rugosa	Roserie de L'Hay
Moss	Madame Delaroche Lambert
China	Hermosa
Species	Pimpinellifolia
Damask	Marchesa Boccella
English	Gertrude Jekyll
Alba	Konigin von Danemark
Centifolia	Fantin-Latour
Hybrid perpetual	Gloire Lyonnaise
Ground cover	Flower Carpet
Ayrshire	Dundee rambler

1. The Chinese
2. Olive trees by the Romans
3. USA, they used the rootstocks from their vines which showed resistance to Phylloxera vastatrix a vine pest which threatened to wipe out the industry
4. Banana
5. Belgium
6. Rhynia, one of the oldest vascular plants found in a 395 million year old Scottish Rynian chert deposit of the Devonian period
7. Former USSR (Spain, Turkey, Syria, Iraq and Afghanistan are also major producers of the roots and leaves of the Glycorrhiza glabra plant)
8. Australia, it is the Kangaroos paw plant
9. Wheat which has been grown in every continent for 7000 years except Antarctica
10. Cucumber

30. SHRUB CROSSWORD #6

```
b e a r b e r r y   p r i v e t   f i r e t h o r n
l     l           o             r
a o u             s a m a r a   i       t r e e
d r e     c f     e             s   b
d n b u s h l o     b r u s h b u s h
e a e     r a f j         h   s
r m a     i n s t a r     e   h
n e n     s n h s         a   w
u n     t e a m w         t   i       c
t t     m l r i i         h   n       h
      a b a f o n t         t         i
s i l k t a s s e l n e c s     p e a r l
p b   r     o     h s       r       e
i r   k     w     a a   s a g e     a
n a       e     l b o x   r       n
d m   m   r   f d u     e     f
l b   i       l e c n i n e   i
e l c a n a r y c l o v e r k   n     r
b e   t       w     t             e
e     b s p i d e r   h           b
r u   r       r   p o p p y       u
r s   s           r               s
y d u t c h m a n s p i p e   n s p a n i s h
```

31. THE ALCOHOLIC GARDEN

Grenadine	Punica granatum
Gin	Juniperus communis
Whisky	Hordeum spp.
Vodka	Solanum tuberosum
Tequilla	Agave sp.
Brandy	Vitis vinifera
Wine	Vitis vinifera
Southern comfort	Prunus persica
Beer	Humulus lupulus
Cider	Malus sp.
Rum	Sacchurum spp.
Perry	Pyrus communis
Cassis	Ribes nigrum
Calvados	Malus sp.
Arak	Palmae sp.
Ouzo	Illicuim verum
Cointreau	Citrus aurantium
Amaretto	Prunus amygdalus
Amarula	Sclerocarya birrea subsp. caffra
Bloody Mary	Lycopersicon esculentum

32/ DOWN THE ALLOTMENT

ANNAGRAM	ANSWER
Rjsauecmreleohakit (9,9)	Jerusalem artichoke
Uaegnbrie (9)	Aubergine
Walfceouilr (11)	Cauliflower
Pyecpneaprene (7,6)	Cayenne pepper
Siehelvsecnea (7,6)	Chinese leaves
Tugoercte (9)	Courgette
Oensvliongeratni (11,5)	Everlasting onion
Eoefnenllrcfne (8,6)	Florence fennel
Yprbshealgumar (7,7)	Hamburg parsley
Herosdihras (11)	Horseradish

Eyinkbadne (6,4)	Kidneybean
Slaichlninhrneopsic (12,7)	Lincolnshire spinach
Ntateumog (9)	Mangetout
Rwtaaoaemprf (9,3)	Marrowfat pea
Pnbhgnaecnoijsninaeuo (8,8,5)	Japanese bunching onion
Lpeubirogocupnrprtclsio (6,9,8)	Purple sprouting broccoli
Hbrbaur (7)	Rhubarb
Rnatnrceueslr (7,6)	Scarlet runner
Obvcasabayge (5,7)	Savoy cabbage
Ereppwtpsee (5,6)	Sweet pepper
Tfekteaaetmbsoo (9,6)	Beefsteak tomato
Esetrsacwr (10)	Watercress
Trcueabtbn (10)	Butterbean
Eopwotstaet (5,6)	Sweetpotato
Rueucmeocurhebgnse (10,8)	Greenhouse cucumber
Dfgsasnrlyie (5,7)	ladysfingers

33. MEGAQUIZ # 2

1. TRUE
2. Flower arranging
3. False (Its an animal)
4. Seaweed
5. Having many spines
6. Aubergine
7. Grasses
8. Strawberries
9. True
10. Container for harvested vegetables
11. False (Red hot poker plant)
12. Thrift, Armeria maritime

13.	Cyperus
14.	Liliaceae
15.	Fasciation
16.	Armilaria mealea
17.	Ulex
18.	To take a soil sample
19.	50°F
20.	True
21.	Maple
22.	Lebanon (The cedar of Lebanon, Cedrus libani)
23.	Foxglove, Digitalis purpurea
24.	Black Pepper
25.	Pimento
26.	Avacado, Persea gratissima
27.	Isatis tinctoria (meaning of dyers)
28.	An Alpine
29.	Gregor Mendel
30.	Canada (Attributed to the genus Gaultheria)
31.	Lawsonia inermis
32.	Polygoacece
33.	Having many leaves
34.	Woody tissue
35.	Cinnamon
36.	Having small flowers
37.	Double flowered (Flore pleno)
38.	Polygonaceae
39.	Beside the sea side
40.	Creeping or prostrate
41.	Of woods or trees
42.	A stand of or collection of Yew trees (Taxus spp.)
43.	Petals
44.	Flabellate
45.	Mares or horses tail
46.	Hips
47.	The carnivorous plant group

48. Yellow

49. Obtained from the plant Palaquium gutta which is used in dentistry adhesives and golf ball coverings

50. Seaweed

51. The seeds or botanically the achene appear on the outer coating of the aggregate fruit

52. Cinchona

53. They have won awards

54. Biological control of whitefly on glasshouse crops

55. Hamamelis mollis

56. Damask roses

57. Tomato

58. Rotovate

59. Monstera

60. Improves aeration and water holding capacity

34/ THE HEALING GARDEN

1. Salix (Salicylic acid), traditionally it was Spirea ulmaria the old name for Fillipendula ulmaria (meadowsweet) that was used hence the word Aspirin from the root Spirea

2. Toothache

3. Hypericum calycinum

4. Chapped nipples

5. Lavender

6. Hops (A hop pillow)

7. To soothe burns or scalds

8. Evening primrose (Oenothera biennis)

9. Aloe vera

10. Sphagnum moss, was used as a field dressing because of its antiseptic properties

35/ CAN YOU GET RID OF THESE MOLES

1. False
2. False
3. True
4. True
5. False
6. False
7. True
8. False
9. False
10. True

36/ TREE AND SHRUB HEADSCRATCHER

j	a	p	a	n	e	s	e	m	a	p	l	e	n	g	l	i	s	h	e	l	m	o	c	k	o
l	d	e	r	i	c	a	t	a	l	p	a	c	h	y	s	a	n	d	r	a	l	e	x	a	r
e	e	e	t	a	x	u	s	b	a	c	c	a	t	a	m	e	l	a	n	c	h	i	e	n	a
n	w	n	o	r	w	a	y	s	p	r	u	c	e	r	a	t	o	s	t	i	g	m	r	d	n
i	s	o	a	t	a	x	o	d	i	u	m	d	i	s	t	i	c	h	u	m	e	a	o	r	g
p	r	r	i	e	r	r	i	a	e	s	c	u	l	u	s	h	i	p	p	o	t	s	s	i	e
h	e	a	r	k	n	i	c	u	m	i	l	e	a	m	i	n	u	t	e	c	a	h	m	a	n
t	m	h	t	a	a	o	i	l	e	x	a	q	u	i	f	o	l	i	v	a	s	i	a	n	i
u	m	s	s	o	v	f	a	n	t	h	u	s	a	l	t	i	s	u	i	s	e	p	r	l	s
o	u	f	i	y	l	e	l	o	l	l	i	s	w	e	e	d	s	m	n	t	q	p	i	a	t
m	s	o	d	e	y	u	i	m	r	i	c	a	n	l	i	i	i	b	e	a	u	o	n	u	a
y	u	e	i	k	s	q	a	s	e	h	o	a	k	s	m	s	m	a	x	n	o	p	u	r	h
e	n	s	r	r	n	n	i	i	m	s	i	l	g	n	e	h	a	c	o	u	i	h	s	e	i
w	g	o	i	u	e	i	h	l	a	e	b	e	t	i	h	w	n	c	c	m	a	a	w	l	s
o	a	r	v	t	p	c	c	e	m	a	m	a	h	s	a	a	n	i	h	o	g	e	e	i	p
l	e	e	a	r	r	y	o	l	o	t	s	i	r	a	v	a	l	f	o	n	l	r	e	q	a
l	a	d	i	o	e	b	b	u	r	h	s	u	b	y	s	i	a	d	r	k	y	h	t	u	n
i	l	l	r	w	c	a	z	e	d	e	p	s	e	l	z	z	u	p	y	e	p	a	c	i	i
w	e	e	a	s	n	h	o	j	t	s	e	d	i	o	b	o	r	t	s	o	t	m	h	d	c
k	l	z	n	i	d	n	u	r	a	i	n	o	l	l	a	c	s	e	d	i	o	n	e	a	a
c	b	a	h	h	c	t	i	w	e	s	e	n	a	p	a	j	u	h	t	u	n	t	s	m	b
o	m	a	r	b	d	e	h	s	a	w	e	t	i	h	w	e	y	r	r	e	b	r	a	b	b
n	r	a	m	l	i	k	c	o	l	m	e	h	n	r	e	t	s	a	e	e	r	t	e	g	a

37/ SOME DEADLY ONES

1. Poppies
2. Asphodel
3. Salt water
4. On Sept 7, 1978, a Bulgarian diplomat Georgi Markow was stabbed with an umbrella on Waterloo Bridge in London. The umbrella fired a tiny pellet into his thigh: the pellet contained ricin and he died a few days later. Ricinus communis is regarded as one of the most deadly plant toxins known.
5. Aconite, is from the plant Monkshood.
6. Deadly nightshade having similar fruits to the garden pea can contaminate crops unseen.
7. Almonds as they contain Arsenic?
8. Banisteriopsis caapi (Liana a jungle climber)
9. Rhubarb. Rheum rhabarbarum
10. Papaver sommniferum, the opium poppy. Chemical formula shown is Morphine.

38. FAIR WEATHER GARDENING

1. The soya bean (very high in sulphur)
2. Clement weather in the morning
3. The white poplar (Populus alba), the leaves are white underneath and when the are showing it is an indication of wind and rain possibly coming.
4. They remain open and colourful in dull weather
5. The flowers close when rain is on the way
6. Rain
7. A harsh winter ahead
8. Horse chestnut (as it is early flowering)
9. They believed that only the wind would open the flowers
10. Snow has been shown to contain higher concentrations of nitrogen, phosphorous and other minerals than ordinary rain water.

39. COMMON TEASERS

Iris	Gladdon
Travellers joy	Clematis
Pink	Carnation
Goutweed	Ground elder
Aster	Michaelmas daisy
Cocksfoot	Orchard grass
Oxlip	Primula
Eglantine	Sweetbriar
Alsike	Clover
Goldenrod	Solidago
Squill	Scilla
Rose of china	Hibiscus
Arum	Cuckoopint
Compassplant	Turpintine plant
Bistort	Snakeroot
Jack by the hedge	Garlic mustard
Greenbriar	Catbriar
London Pride	Saxifrage
Moschatel	Town Hall Clock
Goosefoot	Pigweed
Morning glory	Moon flower
Old mans beard	Clematis
Mullein	Aarons rod
Twitch	Couch grass
Lords and ladies	Arum
Cinquefoil	Potentilla
Monkshood	Aconite
Lunaria	Honesty
Vervain	Verbena
Cleavers	Goosegrass

40. TOOLS

1. Pruning the higher branches of trees and shrubs using an an averruncator, an old fashioned long handles pruner

2. A mattock

3. Tulips

4. Potatoes and beetroot. The tines limit the damage caused to the tubers

5. Paving slabs, a large rubber headed hammer used to set the pavers level

6. Knocking in wooden stakes when fencing

7. The Halberd, a long handled battle axe

8. The Yorkshire billhook has a cutting edge on both sides of the blade

9. A one handed curve bladed saw that cuts on the pull stroke for overhead heavy pruning of tree or shrub branches

10. Tensioning straining or horizontal fencing wires

41. PERENNIALS AND ANNUALS CROSSWORD #8

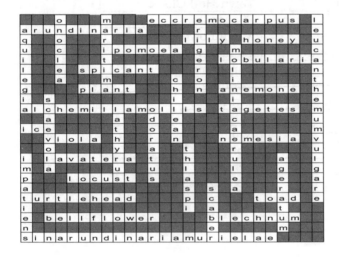

42. KNOW YOUR LIMITS

1. The hedge or field maple (Acer campestris)
2. It is the combination of a hedge and a fence?
3. Trained branches above head height usually using Limes
4. Hedge sparrow
5. Box trees (Buxus spp.)
6. Topiary
7. Hops, Elderberries, sloes, brambles all used for making alcoholic beverages
8. The plant is still in its juvenile state and so protects the new buds from damage.
9. Leylandii hedges
10. It lubricates the shears

43. POND LIFE

1. 5cm of fish per square meter
2. When you place fish in a pond the water turns toxic due to their waste products
3. 1 meter (to let fish run deep to keep warm in winter)
4. Water lilies (He was famous for breeding many new cultivars but when he died his propagation secrets were lost and took many years to rediscover)
5. Japan
6. Peat as it turns sulphurous and contaminates the water. Replace with soil which is clay/slit loam based
7. A marginal aquatic plant
8. They are the fastest growing plants in the aquatic kingdom in order to cope with rising and falling water levels
9. When the oxygenating plants are respiring at night they can suffocate the fish especially in very hot weather when the water is shallow
10. It causes the algae to adhere to each other allowing for easier removal

44. THE BULBOUS JUNGLE

WORDJUMBLE	ANSWER
Enmnaeo (7)	Anemone
Pdlsoeah (8)	Asphodel
Dhidgchenatbiyn (7,8)	Bedding hyacinth
Aioxhnocod (10)	Chionodoxa
Ciomrsaco (9)	Crocosmia
Lvamnlaaolijicaras (11,7)	Convallaria majalis
Wpaomirirlcne (5,8)	Crown imperial
Rnudulcusas (11)	Dracunculus
Blbghelnsuleile (7,8)	English bluebell
Aosliugdl (9)	Gladiolus
Parietmhpsu (11)	Hippeastrum
Anhlyaiehctl (12)	Hyacinthella
Plyodlerllai (7,4)	Leopard lily
Ixiloalyftl (7,4)	Foxtail lily
Tairilaelsrlipaifirmi (11,10)	Fritillaria imperialis
Ihdnonstia (6,4)	Indianshot
Ltsvianuilsgahna (9,7)	Galanthus nivalis
Dnianlymoal (7,4)	Madonna lily
Srsaiuncs (9)	Narcissus
Rilyevnlpuai (8,4)	Peruvian lily
Ncuanlrusu (10)	Ranunculus
Forcsarcusfno (7,6)	Saffron crocus
Lorainctcaspslni (6,3-7)	Scilla non-scripta
Worpndos (8)	Snowdrop
Olywdlsri (5,4)	Sword lily
Ehtitcepcnsaoaeaiazdih (12,10)	Zantedeschia aethiopica

45. LATIN VISITORS

Mole	Talpa europea
Grey Squirrel	Sciurlus carolinensis
Rabbit	Oryctolagus cuniculus
Hedgehog	Erinaceus europaeus
Badger	Meles meles
Deer	Cervus elephas
Fox	Vulpes vulpes
Robin	Erithracus rubecula
Bat	Pipestrelleus pipestrelleus
Cat	Felis silvestris catus

46. THE INDOOR GARDENER

1. By division in order to retain the variegation
2. Echinocactus grussonii
3. By snails and slugs. They produce terrestrial flowers over which the molluscs move carrying pollen between the plants
4. The African violet
5. The orchid (1 gram nearly contains a billion seeds)
6. The edible bread fruit
7. Asparagus sprengeri is not a true fern and therefore do not sporulate
8. Moving them in the house causes their leaves to drop
9. It is the best foliage plant for scrubbing toxins from the atomosphere e.g. carbon monoxide, ethylene etc.
10. So they can fit inside each other for ease of transportation and storage and also easier for plant removal from the pot itself.

47. UNDER THE MICROSCOPE

Boron	B
Copper	Cu
Phosphorus pentoxide	P_2O_5
Magnesium oxide	MgO
Iron	Fe
Pottasium oxide	K_2O
Molybdenum	Mo
Zinc	Zn
Maganese	Mn
Calcium	Ca
Nitrogen	N
Ammonia	NH_3
Nitrite	NO_2^-
Nitrate	NO_3^-

48. FORTY ODD DISCOVERY PLANTFINDER #9

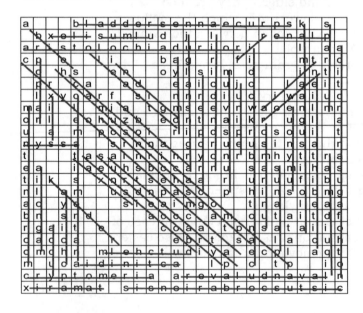

49. COMMON GARDEN CREATURES

Chrysopa carnea	Lacewing
Bombus terrestris	Bumble bee
Macrosiphum rosae	Rose greenfly
Oniscus asellus	Woodlice
Lasius niger	Ant
Talpa europaea	Mole
Adalia bipunctata	2 spotted Ladybird
Erinaceus europaeus	Hedgehog
Erithacus rubecula	Robin
Vanessa atlanta	Red Admiral

50. MEGAQUIZ # 3

1. False, they are terrestrial bromeliads
2. Nettle rash
3. Red Deer
4. Sanseveria trifasciata
5. Camellia sinensis syn. C. theifera
6. Ugli Fruit
7. You will raise the pH?
8. Walnuts?
9. A hardwood
10. Germany, from the german 'welsche' meaning foreign
11. Babylon, 50 km south of Baghdad, Iraq
12. Wellingtonia, Sequoiadendron giganteum (NB not the tallest but the largest by mass of wood)
13. Fencing
14. Chestnut poles
15. The hollow , cylindrical leaves and flowering stems
16. Herbaceous plant (stems and leaves) wither and die and the plant root lies dormant
17. Hardwood cuttings (contains bottom heat for improved rooting)

18. They are poisonous to livestock grazing (Ragwort)
19. Nitrogen, phosphorous, potassium
20. Prevent damping off
21. Causes sudden oak death
22. A cactus
23. Indian shot
24. Carl Von Linneaus
25. An apple
26. Sultanas, raisins, currants
27. approx. 200:1
28. Will not withstand frost
29. Lettuce
30. First early potato
31. Turnip (it's a member of the Brassica family the others being Umbelliferous)
32. Raffia
33. Sweet potato
34. Friable and open structured
35. One spades depth of soil
36. Orchidaceae
37. Jethro Tull
38. Mace
39. Wasp
40. Carrot
41. Asparagus
42. Kapok (the hollow seed fibres were used to manufacture life jackets as they are hollow and have good buoyancy)
43. The immature leaf stalks
44. Neither. It is an herbaceous perennial used as fruit.
45. It is willow used for basket weaving
46. Drumstick primula
47. Okra
48. Ministry of Agriculture, Fisheries and Food
49. Chasselas Doré (It is a Dessert grape the others being wine grapes)
50. Tomatillo

51. Elk horn fern
52. When seed trays show elongated seed growth in the middle of the tray
53. 6.8
54. Marmalade
55. To prevent dehydration of cuttings
56. For planting seedlings of field grown crops
57. Ants
58. Macadamia (is grown in warm climates)
59. Eucalyptus
60. The rule that all plant names shall be called after the person who named them first?

51. SOME TASTY DISHES

1. Summer pudding (Redcurrant, blackcurrant, raspberry and bread)
2. Gardiniera (mixed raw pickle), Cauliflower, carrots, green beans and onions
3. Pesto sauce (Olive oil, basil, garlic and pine nuts)
4. Muesli (Oats, wheat, millet, barley, raisins, almonds, hazelnut)
5. Ratatouille (Garlic, tomato, aubergine, courgette, red pepper)
6. Guacamole (Avocado, Onion, Chilli, Coriander, Tomato, Black pepper)
7. Hummus (Chick peas, Tahini, Lemon, Garlic, Pomegranate seeds, Olive oil, Paprika)
8. Russian Salad (Potato, Carrot, Peas, French Beans, Olive oil, Beetroot and Gherkins)
9. Pineapple upside down cake (Pineapple, Sugar, Cherries, Flour, Vanilla)
10. Waldorf Salad (Apple, Walnut, Celery or Celeriac, Lettuce)

52. FRIEND OR FOE

Ladybirds	Coccinella septempunctata	Friend
Vine weevil	Otiorhynchus sulcatus	Foe
Peach aphid	Brachycaudus schwartzi	Foe
Hover flies	Syrphus ribesii	Friend
Cabbage white	Pieris brassicae	Foe
Bee	Bombus terrestris	Friend
Wasp	Vespula vulgaris	Foe
Earwig	Forficula auricularia	Foe
Woodlouse	Oniscus asellus	Friend
Worm	Lumbriscus terrestris	Friend
New Zealand flat worm	Artioposthia triangulata	Foe
Colorado beetle	Leptinotarsa decemlineata	Foe
Sudden oak death	Phytophthora ramorum	Foe
Crown gall	Agrobacterium tumefaciens	Foe
Toad	Bufo bufo	Friend
Nitrogenase	Nitrogen fixing enzymes	Friend
Slug	Arion hortensis	Foe
Lacewing	Chrysoperla carnea	Friend
Ground beetle	Carabus nemoralis	Friend
Garden spider	Meta segmentat	Friend

53. MATCH EM UP FOR BEGINNERS #10

SPECIFIC EPITHET	DEFINITION
Zebrina	Striped
Rugosa	Wrinkled
Officianalis	Of herbal shops
Palustris	Of the marshes
Revoluta	Rolled back
Mutabilis	Changeable
Imperialis	Powerful
Linguaeform	Tongueshaped
Repens	Creeping
Dolabriforme	Hatchet shaped
Cordata	Heart shaped
Jubatum	Crested/maned
Cochinea	Scarlet
Graminae	Grassy
Lacustris	Found in lakes
Viridiflora	Greenflowered
Vernum	Of spring
Pomerdianum	Post meridian
Trifoliata	Three leaved
Pseudo	False
Papilio	Butterfly flowered
Lupina	Wolf like
Rubicola	Rock inhabiting
Gracillima	Very slender
Fulgens	Gleeming
Maxillare	Jawshaped

54. KEEPING IN SHAPE

Digitate	5 Fingered
Lanceolate	Lance
Lobata	Lobed
Cordate	Heart
Orbicular	Round
Rhomboidal	Diamond
Sagittate	Arrow
Hastate	Spear
Deltoid	Triangular
Dentate	Toothed
Reniform	Kidney
Ensiform	Strap
Filiform	Linear
Pectinate	Comb
Acicular	Needle
Spathulate	Spoon
Crenate	Scalloped
Undulate	Wavy
Flabellate	Fan
Apiculatum	Pointed

55. GARDEN REGULARS (Animals)

MINERS DOG	MOLES
COTTON TAIL	RABBIT
THREE COLOUR MOUSE	SHREW
DOWDY COWS	LADYBIRDS
HEDGE PIG	HEDGEHOG
BROCK	BADGER
CUSHET	WOOD PIGEON
HALCYON	KINGFISHER
DUNNOCK	HEDGE SPAROW
MAD APPLE	EGGPLANT

56. COLLECTIVE NOUNS

COLONY	ANTS
SWARM	BEES
FLIGHT	BUTTERFLIES
ARMY	CATERPILLARS
CLOWDER	CATS
SKULK	FOXEZ
CLOUD	GOLDFISH
HORDE	KNATS
ARRAY	HEDGEHOGS
TIDING	MAGPIES
KIT	PIGEONS
BUILDING	ROOKS
MURMURATION	STARLINGS
HOST	SPARROWS
PITYING	TURTLEDOVES
SCHOOL	GOLDFISH

57. KNOCK THE SPOTS OFF THIS!

7 Spotted	*Coccinella septempunctata*
2 Spotted	*Adalia bipunctata*
10 Spotted	*Adalia decempunctata*
11 Spotted	*Coccinella undecimpunctata*
18 Spotted	*Myrrha octodecimguttata*
22 Spotted	*Psyllobora (Thea) vigintiduopunctata*
14 Spotted	*Propylea quattuordecimpunctata*
16 Spotted	*Tytthaspis (Micraspis) sedecimpunctata*
24 Spotted	*Subcoccinella vigintiquattuorpunctata*
13 Spotted	*Hippodamia tredecimguttata*
5 Spotted	*Coccinella quinquepunctata*

58. TREE AND SHRUB MIX EM UP

GENUS	SPECIES	CV./VARIETY
Acer	japonicum	Aureum
Aucba	japonica	Variegate
Berberis	ottawensis	Purpurea
Clematis	orientalis	Orangepeel
Cornus	alba	Sibirica
Deutzia	scabra	Plena
Euonymus	fortunei	Radiacans
Fraxinus	excelsior	Pendula
Ginkgo	biloba	Faastigiata
Hydrangea	serrata	Bluebird
Ilex	Aquifolium	Bassiflava
Juniperus	Squamata	Meyeri
Kerria	Japonica	Pleniflora
Lonicera	Nitida	Baggesensgold
Magnolia	Soulangeana	Rubra
Picea	Pungens	Kosta
Prunus	triloba	Multiplex
Rhus	Glabra	Laciniata
Rosmarianus	Officianalis	Albus
Salix	Alba	Chermesina
Sorbus	Aria	Lutescens
Syringa	Vulgaris	Charles x
Taxus	Baccata	Ellegantissima
Tsuga	Canadensis	Cole
Ulex	Europaeus	Plenus
Wisteria	floribunda	macrobotrys

59. CLIMBING UP THE WALL

1. Chile (Chilean glory vine)
2. Just after it has flowered in the spring
3. Its thorns
4. Wistaria (Wisteria is a misnomer as it is named after Wistar)
5. Polygonum baldschuanicum
6. Kent
7. A hop garden
8. It slows the sap down and they form more flower buds
9. Chinese gooseberries (Kiwi fruit)
10. Hops

60. DO YOU KNOW YOU APPLES

Cox's orange pippin	Dessert
Lane's Prince Albert	Cooker
Bramley's seedling	Cooker
Newton wonder	Cooker
Red Soldier	Cider
Laxton's superb	Dessert
Charles Ross	Dessert
American mother	Dessert
Grenedier	Cooker
Sweet coppin	Cider
Worcester permain	Dessert
Blenheim Orange	Dessert
Granny smith	Dessert
Egremont russet	Dessert
Diamond Jubilee	Cooker
Tremlitts Bitter	Cider
Reinette de Canada	Cooker
James Grieve	Dessert
Kingston black	Cider
Court Pendu Plat	Dessert

61. ON THE FUCHSIA TRIAL

Avocet	Bush
Triphylla	Cluster
Cascade	Trailing
Alice Hoffman	Bush
Marinka	Trailing
Ting-a-Ling	Bush
Mission Bells	Bush
Pink Galore	Trailing
Rufus the Red	Bush
Thalia	Cluster
Winston Churchill	Bush
Swingtime	Trailing
Summer Snow	Trailing
Golden Treasure	Bush
Flash	Cluster
Sunray	Bush
Tom Thumb	Bush
Tom West	Trailing
Mrs Popple	Bush
Auntie Jinks	Trailing

62. BLUE FOR YOU

Cyananthus microphyllus	Trailing bell flower
Gentiana farreri	Gentian
Lithospermum oleifolium	Gromwell
Primula marginata 'Linda Pope'	Rockery Primrose
Veronica rupestris	Rockery Speedwell
Campanula calycanthema	Canterbury Bells

BLUE FOR YOU contd.

Cobaea scandens	Cathedral Bell
Convolvulus 'Royal Ensign'	Morning Glory
Nemophila menziesii	Baby Blue Eyes
Myosotis alpestris	Forget me not
Nigella damascene 'Miss Jeckyll'	Love in a Mist
Agapanthus campulatus 'Isis'	African Lilly
Aconitum 'Sparks Variety'	Monkshood
Anchusa 'Dropmore'	Alkanet
Catananche caerulea	Cupids Dart
Echinops ritro	Globe Thistle
Omphalodes cappadocica	Naval Wort
Platycodon grandiflorum mariesii	Balloon Flower
Polemonium caeruleum	Jacobs Ladder
Veronica gentianoides	Speedwell

63. THE NAMES THE SAME

Tacca	Bat plant
Mentha	Catmint
Beloperone gutta	Shrimp plant
Primula veris	Cowslip
Mimulus	Monkey Flower
Erigeron	Flea Bane
Cardamine	Cuckoo Flower

THE NAMES THE SAME contd.

Aruncus	Goats Beard
Strelitzia reginae	Bird of Paradise
Linaria	Toad Flax
Auricaria auracana	Monkey Puzzle
Quercus cerris	Turkey Oak
Clemone spinosa	Spider flower
Coreopsis	Tickseed
Lychnis	Ragged Robin
Delphinium	Larkspur
Acanthus	Bears Breeches
Cimicifuga	Snake Root
Antennaria	Cats Ear
Doronicum	Leopards Bane
Eremurus	Foxtail Lilly

64. CAN YOU SEE A RAINBOW

Sequoia sempervirens	Redwood
Sorbus aria	Whitebeam
Betula pendula	Silver birch
Fagus sylvatica	Copper beech
Eucalyptus globules	Blue gum
Gaultheria	Wintergreen
Laburnum	Goldenrain
Populus alba	White poplar
Prunus spinosa	Blackthorn
Tillia cordata	Lime
Caryopteris	Blue Spirea
Choisya	Mexican orange blossom
Decaisnea fargesii	Blue Bean
Halesia	Silver Bell

Indigofera	Indigo
Philadelphus	Mock orange
Syringa	Lilac
Santolina	Lavender cotton
Abies	Silver fir
Cedrus atlantica glauca	Blue cedar

65. IN AND AROUND THE POND

Aponogeton	Deep water	Water Hawthorn
Lemna	Floaters	Duckweed
Fontinalis	Oxygenators	Willow Grass
Acorus	Marginal	Sweet Flag
Trollius	Bog	Globe Flower
Nymphoides	Deep water	Water Fringe
Glyceria	Marginal	Water Grass
Lagarosiphon	Floaters	Goldfish Weed
Urticularia	Floaters	Bladderwort
Orontium	Deep water	Golden Club
Polygonum	Bog	Knotweed
Hydrocharis	Floaters	Frog-bit
Potamogeton	Floaters	Pond weed
Lysichiton	Bog	Skunk Cabbage
Cotula	Marginal	Golden Buttons
Elodea	Floaters	Canadian Pond weed
Nuphar	Deep water	Pond Lily
Stratiotes	Floaters	Water soldier
Onoclea	Bog	Sensitive Fern
Menyanthus	Marginal	Bog Bean

66. FOOD FOR FREE

Blackberry	Rubus fruiticosus
Elderberry	Sambucus nigra
Sloe	Prunus spinosa
Green Gage	Prunus italica
Damson	Prunus damascena
Field mushroom	Agaricus campestris
Wild garlic	Alliaria petiolata
Hazelnut	Corylus avellana
Nettle	Urtica dioica
Alexanders	Smrynium olusatium
Hop	Humulus lupulus
Marsh Samphire	Salicornia europea
Sorrel	Rumex acetosa
Horseradish	Armoracia rusticana
Crab apple	Malus sylvestris
Giant puff ball	Langermannia gigantean
Medlar	Mespilus germanica
Black walnut	Juglans nigra
Dandeloin	Taraxacum officinale
Wild raspberry	Rubus idaeus

67. NUTS ABOUT NUTS

Peanut	Arachis hypogea
Macadamia	Macadamia turnifolia
Walnut	Juglans nigra
Hazelnut	Corylus avelana
Almond	Prunus amygdalus
Sweet Chestnut	Castanea sativa
Pine nut	Pinus spp.
Pistachio	Pistacia vera
Pecan	Carya illinoensis
Cashew	Anacardium occidentale

NUTS ABOUT NUTS contd.

Coconut	Coccus nucifera
Goat nut	Simmondsia chinensis
Brazil nut	Bertholletia excelsa
Heart nut	Juglans sieboldiana
Palm nut	Elaeis guinneensis
Nutmeg	Parkia Africana
Shea nut	Butyrospermum parki
Snake nut	Ophiocaryon paradoxum
Bread nut	Brosimum alicastrum
Beech nut	Fagus sylvatica

68. MEGA STATE TO BE IN

Alabama	Camellia
Arkansas	Apple blossom
Conneticut	Mountain Laurel
Delamare	Peach Blossom
Florida	Orange Blossom
Georgia	Cherokee Rose
Kentucky	Goldenrod
Louisiana	Magnolia
Maine	Tassle
Maryland	Thunbergia
Massachusetts	Arbutus
Mississippi	Magnolia
New Hampshire	Purple Lilac
New Jersey	Purple Violet
New York	Rose
North Carolina	Flowering Dogwood
Oklahoma	Mistletoe
Pennsylvania	Mountain Laurel
Rhode Island	Violet
South Carolina	Carolina jessamine
Tennessee	Iris

MEGA STATE TO BE IN contd.

Texas	Blue Bonnet
Vermont	Red Clover
Virginia	Flowering Dogwood
West Virginia	Rhododendron
Illinois	Native Violet
Indiana	Peony
Iowa	Wild Rose
Kansas	Sunflower
Michigan	Apple Blossom
Minnesota	Pink and White Lady's Slipper
Missouri	Hawthorn
Nebraska	Golden Rod
North Dakota	Wild Prairie Rose
Ohio	Scarlet Carnation
South Dakota	American Pasque Flower
Wisconsin	Wood Violet
Alaska	Forget-me-not
Arizona	Saguaro
California	Golden Poppy
Colorado	Rocky Mountain Columbine
Hawaii	Hibiscus
Idaho	Syringa
Montana	Bitter Root
Nevada	Sage Brush
New Mexico	Yucca
Oregon	Oregon Grape
Utah	Sego Lily
Washington	Coast Rhododendron
Wyoming	Indian Paintbrush

69. MUSICAL CRYPTIC PLANTS

1. Red hot chilli peppers
2. Guns and roses
3. Wheatus
4. Hazel O 'Connor
5. Lou Read
6. Robert Plant
7. Cranberries
8. Beach Boys
9. Hot House Flowers
10. Black eyed peas

70. RIPARIAN RASCALS

Zantedeschia	Arum
Sparganium	Bur-Reed
Veronica	Brooklime
Typha	Reedmace
Ranunculus	Water Buttercup
Sagittaria	Arrowhead
Peltandra	Arrow Arum
Saururus	Lizards Tail
Myosotis	Water Forget-me-not
Scirpus	Bullrush
Pontederia	Pickerel Weed
Myriophyllum	Parrots feather
Mimulus	Monkey Flower
Juncus	Rush
Mentha	Water Mint
Hypericum	Marsh St. Johns Wort
Eriophorum	Cotton Grass
Cyperus	Umbrella grass
Carex	Sedge
Caltha	Marsh Marigold

71. GET BUSY WITH THE BEES

1. Nectar and pollen
2. Pollen
3. The honey flow
4. Drone, worker and queen
5. Hymenoptera
6. The wax is secreted from the abdomen of the bees from 8 glands from the underside. Wax is made in small scales or chips and before being used is mixed with bee saliva and pollen.
7. A buzzying
8. A row of bees known as ventilator bees line the entrance of the hive and force in cool air by beating their wings.
9. Honeycombs, beeswax, 6 sides.
10. Upto 3,000
11. Propolis
12. Both prolific bee eaters
13. White or dutch clover
14. Nutmeg all of the others have been used to treat wasp stings
15. Fine weather
16. Apiarist
17. Worker
18. Royal Jelly
19. 16 days
20. It is unfertilised

72. MIND YOU PEAS AND B'S

Vicia faba	Windsor or broadbean
Phaseolus vulgare	Common American bean
Phaseolus lunatus	Lima or butter bean
Phaseolus aureus	Mung bean

Vigna sinensis	Cow pea
Glycine soja	Soy bean
Dolichos lablab	Bonavist bean
Phaseolus coccineus	Runner bean
Dolichos biflorus	Horsegram bean
Pisum sativum	English pea
Lathyrus odoratus	Sweet pea
Tingitanus	Tangier pea
Carbanzo	Chick pea
Sicer arietinum	Spanish pea
Cajanus indicum	Pigeon pea
Lotus tetragonolobus	Asparagus pea
Canavalia ensiformis	Jack bean
Cyamopsis psoraloides	Cluster bean
Phaseolus mungo	Black gram bean
Canavalia gladiata	Sword bean

73. SOW YOUR SEEDS

Sunflower	Helianthus
Poppy	Papaver
Sesame	Sesamum indicum
Pumpkin	Cucurbita mixta
Carroway	Carum carvi
Corriander	Corriandrum sativa
Cumin	Cuminum syminum
Wheat	Triticum spp.
Sweet corn	Zea mays
Oats	Avena sativa
Fennell	Foeniculum vulgare
Musturd	Brassica napus
Cardamom	Elettaria cardamumom
Fenugreek	Triganella foenom-graecum
Black pepper	Piper nigra
Garden pea	Pisum sativum

SOW YOUR SEEDS contd.

Lentils	Lens culinaris
Rice	Oryza sativa
Barley	Hordeum spp.
Peanut	Arachis hypogaea

74. WILD WHO AM I?

1. Travellers joy
2. Field poppy
3. Wild radish
4. Shepherds purse
5. Watercress
6. Red Campion
7. Ragged Robin
8. Chickweed
9. Hottentot fig
10. Wood sorrel
11. Himalayan balsam
12. Birds-foot-trefoil
13. Meadowsweet
14. Ladys mantle
15. Commen sorrel
16. Scarlet Pimpernel
17. Deadly nightshade
18. Bluebell
19. Oxeye daisy
20. Common twayblade

75. FILL IN THE BLANKS GARDEN PROVERBS

1. Gardener, garden
2. Tree, lie
3. Oaks, acorns
4. Clover
5. Nettle, rose
6. Lily

FILL IN THE BLANKS GARDEN PROVERBS contd.

7. Rose, thorn
8. Winds, showers, flowers
9. Daises, spring
10. Bed, head
11. Forget, dry, wet
12. Gorse, kissing
13. Pears
14. Trees, hold, winter, cold
15. Weeds day

76. MORE TASTY DISHES

Country	Meat/Veg	Plant Ingredients	Dish
India	Chicken	Ginger, garlic, chilli, tumeric, lemon, coriander, garam masala	Chicken Tikka
Morocco	Lamb	Onion, parsley, coriander, mint, cumin, mixed spice, paprika, black pepper	Lamb Keftas
Mexico	Veg	Red Kidney beans, onion, garlic, bay, Serrano chilli, corn oil, tomato	Frijoles
Spain	Veg	Bell Pepper, cucumber, onion, chilli, plum tomatoes, olive oil, black pepper	Gazpacho

Mexico	Veg	Corn	Tortillas
Greece	Veg	Chick peas, lemon, garlic, olive oil, cayenne pepper, tahini, black pepper, parsley	Hummus
Ireland	Lamb	Onion, carrot, potato, thyme, parsley, black pepper	Irish stew
Thailand	Veg	Wheat, sugar, coconut, sesame, banana	Thai fried bananas
Thailand	Veg	Tapioca	Tapioca pudding
Italy	Veg	Polenta flower, olive oil, onion, nutmeg, parsley, black pepper	Polenta
Italy	Veg	Red onion, olives, flour, yeast, parsley or mint	Olive bread
Japan	Veg	Mooli, flour, sweet potato, carrot, shiitake mushroom, French beans, red pepper	Tempura

BIOGRAPHY

Robin Rowlinson has worked in horticultural education for many years and specialises in glasshouse crops and garden art.

Jonathan MacDonald lectures on a wide range of subjects and currently runs the full time horticulture education programme at Reaseheath college in the UK.

THE INQUISITIVE GARDENER

VOLUME 2

"Even more amazing fun trivia for series gardeners"

AVAILABLE BY MAIL ORDER

TO ORDER PLEASE SEND £7.99
INCLUDING POSTAGE AND
PACKAGING TO:

R&M Publishing
65 Bramhall Road
CREWE
CHESHIRE
UK

Please make cheques payable to: R&M
Publishing.

Or email: **jnthnma8@aol.com** to order
your copy.